IGMacdonald

November 1963

THE THEORY OF ORDINARY
DIFFERENTIAL EQUATIONS

UNIVERSITY MATHEMATICAL TEXTS

GENERAL EDITORS

ALEXANDER C. AITKEN, D.Sc., F.R.S.

DANIEL E. RUTHERFORD, D.Sc., Dr. Math.

———

THE THEORY OF ORDINARY
DIFFERENTIAL EQUATIONS

J. C. BURKILL
Sc.D., F.R.S.

FELLOW OF PETERHOUSE, AND READER IN MATHEMATICAL ANALYSIS IN
THE UNIVERSITY OF CAMBRIDGE

OLIVER AND BOYD

EDINBURGH AND LONDON
NEW YORK: INTERSCIENCE PUBLISHERS, INC.

1962

First Published 1956

Second Edition 1962

PRINTED IN HOLLAND BY N.V. DIJKSTRA'S DRUKKERIJ,
VOORHEEN BOEKDRUKKERIJ GEBROEDERS HOITSEMA, GRONINGEN
FOR OLIVER AND BOYD LTD., EDINBURGH

PREFACE

Most students of mathematics, science and engineering realise that the list of standard forms of differential equations which is presented to them as admitting of explicit integration is giving them little insight into the general topic of differential equations and their solutions.

Equations as simple as

$$y' = 1 + xy^2$$

and
$$y'' = xy$$

cannot be solved by finite combinations of algebraic, exponential and trigonometric functions, and many of the equations which occur in the mathematical expression of natural phenomena cannot be reduced to any of the soluble forms.

The object of this text is to outline the theory of which the standard types are special cases. We shall see, among other things, that many properties of solutions of differential equations can be deduced directly from the equations. We shall also develop methods of finding solutions expressed as infinite series or as integrals. This material has so far been available to the student only in more substantial books on Differential Equations or in chapters of treatises on the Theory of Functions.

The theory of differential equations has a high educational value for the second or third year undergraduate. Here he will find straightforward and natural applications of the ideas and theorems of mathematical analysis. Solutions of equations in infinite series require the investigation of convergence. Again, some parts of the theory are seen in a clearer light if the variables are supposed to be complex and the concepts of branch point, analytic continuation and contour integration are used.

I have tried to keep in mind that this is a text-book and not a treatise. Results are stated in the most useful rather than the most general form. In Chapter I, for instance, the basic existence theorem is proved, and then various developments and extensions are indicated without detailed proof.

This text is closely related to others in the series. Ince's text includes the necessary background of explicit integration of the simple types of differential equations. The texts of Hyslop on Infinite Series and Phillips on Functions of a Complex Variable contain the theorems in these subjects that will be applied. Sneddon's account of Special Functions gives properties of Legendre, Bessel and other functions from a standpoint rather different from ours.

Some of the examples were set in the Mathematical Tripos and are reprinted by permission of the Cambridge University Press. I am grateful to the general editors and to the publishers for including this book in their series, and to Dr. Rutherford for his careful scrutiny of the manuscript and proof-sheets.

CAMBRIDGE,   J. C. B.
   September 1955.

PREFACE TO THE SECOND EDITION

An appendix has been added on Laplace transforms and one on the equation $Pdx + Qdy + Rdz = 0$. The interest of these topics may be manipulative rather than theoretical, but the student who wishes to be informed on them will be spared the necessity of turning to a different book.

May 1961.   J. C. B.

CONTENTS

CHAPTER V

SINGULARITIES OF EQUATIONS

CHAPTER VI

CONTOUR INTEGRAL SOLUTIONS

CHAPTER VII

LEGENDRE FUNCTIONS

CHAPTER I

EXISTENCE OF SOLUTIONS

1. Some problems for investigation. In a first course on Differential Equations the student learns to recognize certain types which can be solved by finite combinations of functions known to him (algebraic, trigonometric etc.). An account of methods of solving these standard forms of differential equations can be found in Ince's book, *Integration of Ordinary Differential Equations*, in this series of mathematical texts. This book will be referred to as Ince's Text and the comprehensive work by the same writer, *Ordinary Differential Equations* (Longmans, Green, 1927) as Ince's Treatise.

There are many differential equations, simple in appearance, which are not reducible to any of the standard forms. For example, neither of the equations

$$y' = 1 + xy^2,$$
$$y'' = xy$$

can be solved by a finite combination of elementary functions.

This suggests the first problem which calls for investigation. Under what conditions can we assert that a given differential equation possesses solutions, apart from our ability to express the solutions in a particular form? This problem will be taken up in § 3.

A typical problem at a later stage will be to discover properties of solutions of an equation even when it is impossible or inconvenient to obtain explicit expressions for them. Chapter III contains investigations of this kind.

It is always open to us to extend the list of functions

which are regarded as available for solving differential equations. If an equation, not of one of the standard forms, has many applications, say to problems of physics, it may be worth while to give names to its solutions and thus define new functions; we can study their properties and make tables of their values. The equation $y'' = xy$ just mentioned (Airy's equation), which presents itself in problems of diffraction, gives rise to functions called $Ai(x)$ and $Bi(x)$. These functions lie outside the scope of this book, but an account will be given in Chapters VII and VIII of the more important functions, Legendre's and Bessel's, arising from differential equations which occur repeatedly in applied mathematics.

2. Simple ideas about solutions. Consider the first-order equation

$$y' = f(x, y). \tag{2.1}$$

To solve this equation we have to find the functions $y = y(x)$ which satisfy it for all values of x in an appropriate interval, say $a - h \leqq x \leqq a + h$. The geometrical interpretation is that the curve $y = y(x)$ has at every point a tangent whose gradient is determined by (2.1).

Geometrical intuition leads us to expect that a solution will exist through a given point $x = a$, $y = b$, and that we can construct the curve representing it by a process such as the following. Draw a short segment of a straight line from (a, b) with gradient $f(a, b)$ to the point (x_1, y_1). From (x_1, y_1) draw a short segment with gradient $f(x_1, y_1)$ to (x_2, y_2); and so on, to (x_n, y_n) say. We thus follow the gradient prescribed by the differential equation. It is at least plausible that, as the lengths of the segments in the construction are decreased, the polygons will approximate to a curve for which $y' = f(x, y)$.

These indications, which do not profess to prove anything, can be developed into a formal argument. We shall in fact adopt a rather different approach to the existence theorem.

Simple geometrical considerations will often yield quickly rough graphs of solutions of an equation.

The following examples illustrate these introductory remarks and lead up to the general existence-theorem, which will be stated in § 3.

Example 1.

$$y' + 2xy = 1.$$

This is a linear equation, with integrating factor e^{x^2}. It has the solution

$$y = e^{-x^2} \int_a^x e^{t^2} \, dt,$$

where a is an arbitrary constant. This integral cannot be integrated in terms of elementary functions, but it defines a function of x, and a unique solution of the equation exists through any assigned point of the (x, y) plane.

The reader may use this example for practice in the drawing of rough graphs of solutions. Note the following facts.

(a) The locus of points for which $y' = $ constant is the rectangular hyperbola $1 - 2xy = $ constant. In particular $y' = 0$ (the locus of the maxima and minima of the solutions of the differential equation) gives $xy = \frac{1}{2}$. Also $y' = 1$ on either axis. Sketch $xy = \frac{1}{2}$ and (say) $xy = \pm 1$ as guides.

(b) Differentiating, we find that

$$y'' + 2x + 2y - 4x^2 y = 0.$$

The sign of y'' for a given (x, y) determines whether the solution is convex or concave, and, in particular, the locus of inflexions of the solutions is

$$y = \frac{x}{2x^2 - 1}.$$

Sketch this as a further guide.

It is now easy, starting at any point and following the value of y', to draw the solution through that point. It will be found that all solutions are asymptotic to the x-axis, from above as $x \to + \infty$ and from below as $x \to - \infty$.

Example 2.

$$y' = f(x), \text{ where } f(x) = 0 \text{ for } x < 0$$
$$\text{and} \quad f(x) = 1 \text{ for } x \geqq 0.$$

The equation has no solution valid for $x = 0$. The function y defined by $y = C$ for $x < 0$ and $y = x + C$ for $x \geqq 0$ is a continuous function satisfying the equation for all other values of x, but it has no derivative at $x = 0$. Plainly the failure is due to the discontinuity of $f(x)$.

Example 3.

$$y' = 3y^{2/3}, \text{ given that } y = 0 \text{ for } x = 0.$$

There is no unique solution, for $y = x^3$ and $y = 0$ both satisfy the requirements.

More elaborate examples can be constructed of equations $y' = f(x, y)$, with $f(x, y)$ continuous, having infinitely many solutions through an assigned point (see example 10 at the end of this chapter).

Example 4.

$$y' = 1 + xy^2 \text{ with } y = 0 \text{ for } x = 0.$$

This is a Riccati equation (Ince, Text, p. 22) and we should need to know a particular solution to reduce it according to the standard method to an integrable form.

We shall instead use this example to illustrate the construction of a solution as an infinite series by a method of successive approximations. It is just this method which will be used to establish the general existence theorem.

Let us denote by $y_0, y_1, y_2, \ldots$ successive approximations to y, where

$$y'_{n+1} = 1 + xy_n^2.$$

Then, if we choose $y_0 = 0$, we obtain

$$y_1' = 1, \qquad\qquad y_1 = x;$$
$$y_2' = 1 + x^3, \qquad\qquad y_2 = x + \frac{x^4}{4};$$
$$y_3' = 1 + x^3 + \frac{x^6}{2} + \frac{x^9}{16}; \qquad y_3 = x + \frac{x^4}{4} + \frac{x^7}{14} + \frac{x^{10}}{160}.$$

We can continue this process as far as we like and it appears likely to give a good approximation to the true value of the solution, at least for small values of x.

3. Existence of a solution.

After these introductory remarks we are now in a position to state the main result of this chapter. We need one definition.

Lipschitz condition. A function $\varphi(y)$ is said to satisfy the Lipschitz condition in a given interval if there is a constant A such that

$$|\varphi(y_1) - \varphi(y_2)| \leqq A|y_1 - y_2|$$

for every pair of values y_1, y_2 in the interval.

We observe that the condition is certainly satisfied if $|\varphi'(y)| \leqq A$. Its usefulness is that it leads to much the same consequences as the hypothesis of a bounded derivative, but the restrictive assumption that the derivative exists at every point is avoided.

THEOREM 1. *Let $f(x, y)$ be continuous in a domain D of the (x, y) plane and let M be a constant such that $|f(x, y)| < M$ in D. Let $f(x, y)$ satisfy in D the Lipschitz condition in y,*

$$|f(x, y_1) - f(x, y_2)| \leqq A |y_1 - y_2|,$$

where the constant A is independent of x, y_1, y_2.

Let the rectangle R, defined by

$$|x - a| \leqq h, \quad |y - b| \leqq k,$$

lie in D, where $Mh < k$. Then, for $|x - a| \leqq h$, the differential equation

$$y' = f(x, y)$$

has a unique solution $y = y(x)$ for which $b = y(a)$.

PROOF. Define the sequence of functions

$$y_0(x) = b,$$

$$y_1(x) = b + \int_a^x f\{t, y_0(t)\}dt,$$

$$y_2(x) = b + \int_a^x f\{t, y_1(t)\}dt,$$

$$\cdot \quad \cdot \quad \cdot \quad \cdot \quad \cdot \quad \cdot \quad \cdot \quad \cdot \quad \cdot \quad \cdot \quad \cdot$$

$$y_n(x) = b + \int_a^x f\{t, y_{n-1}(t)\}dt.$$

We shall prove that, as $n \to \infty$, $\lim y_n(x)$ gives the required solution. There are several steps in the proof.

(i) *We prove that, for $a - h \leqq x \leqq a + h$, the curve $y = y_n(x)$ lies in the rectangle R, that is to say $b - k < y < b + k$.*

The proof is inductive. If $y = y_{n-1}(x)$ lies in R, then

$$|y_n(x) - b| = \left| \int_a^x f\{t, y_{n-1}(t)\}dt \right|$$
$$\leqq M|x - a| \leqq Mh < k.$$

The same argument shows that $|y_1(x) - b| < k$, and the assertion therefore holds for all n.

(ii) *We prove, again by induction, that*

$$|y_n(x) - y_{n-1}(x)| \leqq \frac{MA^{n-1}}{n!} |x - u|^n.$$

Suppose that this inequality holds with $n - 1$ in place of n. Then

$$y_n(x) - y_{n-1}(x) = \int_a^x \{f(t, y_{n-1}) - f(t, y_{n-2})\}dt.$$

The modulus of the integrand is at most $A|y_{n-1}(t) - y_{n-2}(t)|$ and so, by the induction hypothesis, at most equal to $MA^{n-1}|t - a|^{n-1}/(n - 1)!$ Therefore

$$|y_n(x) - y_{n-1}(x)| \leqq \frac{MA^{n-1}}{(n-1)!} \left| \int_a^x |t - a|^{n-1}dx \right| = \frac{MA^{n-1}}{n!} |x - a|^n.$$

For $n = 1$, $|y_1(x) - b| \leqq \left| \int_a^x f(t, b)dt \right| \leqq M|x - a|$ and so the inequality holds for all n.

(iii) *The sequence $y_n(x)$ converges uniformly to a limit for $a - h \leqq x \leqq a + h$.*

From (ii) the terms of the series

$$b + \{y_1(x) - b\} + \ldots + \{y_n(x) - y_{n-1}(x)\} + \ldots$$

are numerically less than those of the convergent series

$$b + Mh + \ldots + \frac{MA^{n-1}h^n}{n!} + \ldots$$

By the Weierstrass M-test, the former series converges uniformly for $a - h \leqq x \leqq a + h$, and since its terms are continuous functions of x, its sum, $\lim\limits_{n \to \infty} y_n(x) = y(x)$ say, is continuous.†

(iv) $y = y(x)$ *satisfies the differential equation* $y' = f(x, y)$.

Since $y_n(x)$ tends uniformly to $y(x)$ in $(a - h, a + h)$ and

$$| f(x, y) - f(x, y_n) | \leqq A | y - y_n |,$$

it follows that $f\{x, y_n(x)\}$ tends uniformly to $f\{x, y(x)\}$.

By letting $n \to \infty$ in the equation

$$y_n(x) = b + \int_a^x f\{t, y_{n-1}(t)\}dt,$$

we deduce that

$$y(x) = b + \int_a^x f\{t, y(t)\}dt.$$

The integrand on the right-hand side is a continuous function of t, and so the integral has the derivative $f(x, y)$. Hence $y'(x) = f(x, y)$. Also $y(a) = b$.

(v) *Uniqueness of the solution.* We now prove that the solution $y = y(x)$ just found is the only solution for which $y(a) = b$.

For suppose there is another, $y = Y(x)$ say, and let $|Y(x) - y(x)| \leqq B$ when $a - h \leqq x \leqq a + h$. (We can certainly take $B = 2k$). Then

$$Y(x) - y(x) = \int_a^x [f\{t, Y(t)\} - f\{t, y(t)\}]dt.$$

But

$$|f\{t, Y(t)\} - f\{t, y(t)\} | \leqq A | Y(t) - y(t) | \leqq AB.$$

Therefore

$$| Y(x) - y(x) | \leqq AB | x - a |.$$

We can repeat the argument, obtaining successively as upper bounds for $| Y(x) - y(x) |$ in $(a - h, a + h)$ the expressions

$$\frac{A^2 B}{2!} | x - a |^2, \dots \quad , \quad \frac{A^n B}{n!} | x - a |^n, \dots$$

† See Hyslop, *Infinite Series*, pp. 70, 73.

But this sequence tends to 0 and so $Y(x) = y(x)$ in $(a - h, a + h)$, and the proof of the theorem is complete.

A slightly different version of the above theorem is sometimes useful; we state it as a Corollary.

COROLLARY. *Let $f(x, y)$ be continuous for $\alpha \leqq x \leqq \beta$ and all y. Let it satisfy the Lipschitz condition of the theorem. Then, given a, b, with $\alpha \leqq a \leqq \beta$, the equation $y' = f(x, y)$ has a unique solution $y = y(x)$ for $\alpha \leqq x \leqq \beta$ for which $b = y(a)$.*

To establish the corollary we adapt the argument of theorem 1 by omitting the step (i) and defining the M in (ii) and (iii) to be the upper bound of $|f(x, b)|$ for $\alpha \leqq x \leqq \beta$.

4.   Extensions of the existence theorem. The basic existence theorem of § 3 may be elaborated in a number of ways, some of which will be outlined.

THEOREM 2. *With the hypotheses of Theorem 1, suppose that $y = Y(x)$ is the solution for which $Y(a) = b + \delta$. Then, for $|x - a| \leqq h$,*

$$|Y(x) - y(x)| \leqq \delta e^{Ah}.$$

This means that a small change in the initial conditions causes only a small change in the solution throughout an interval.

PROOF. Construct a sequence $Y_n(x)$ by the rules

$$Y_0(x) = b + \delta,$$
$$Y_1(x) = b + \delta + \int_a^x f\{t, Y_0(t)\}dt,$$
$$\cdot \quad \cdot \quad \cdot \quad \cdot \quad \cdot \quad \cdot \quad \cdot \quad \cdot \quad \cdot \quad \cdot \quad \cdot \quad \cdot \quad \cdot \quad \cdot \quad \cdot$$
$$Y_n(x) = b + \delta + \int_a^x f\{t, Y_{n-1}(t)\}dt.$$

As before, $Y_n(x)$ converges to the solution $Y(x)$.

$$|Y_1(x) - y_1(x)| \leqq \delta + \left| \int_a^x |f(t, b + \delta) - f(t, b)| \, dt \right|$$
$$\leqq \delta + A\delta |x - a|.$$

$$| Y_2(x) - y_2(x) | \leqq \delta + \left| \int_a^x | f\{t, Y_1(t)\} - f\{t, y_1(t)\} | \, dt \right|$$

$$\leqq \delta + A\delta | x - a | + \tfrac{1}{2} A^2 \delta | x - a |^2.$$

By induction,

$$| Y_n(x) - y_n(x) | \leqq \delta + A\delta | x - a | + \ldots + \frac{A^n \delta}{n!} | x - a |^n$$

$$\leqq \delta e^{A |x - a|} \leqq \delta e^{Ah}.$$

Let $n \to \infty$ and the theorem is proved.

By similar arguments it can be proved that the solutions of an equation

$$y' = f(x, y, \lambda)$$

vary continuously with the parameter λ.

Our next extension is to a system of simultaneous differential equations. The ideas are shown if we take two equations

$$\left. \begin{array}{ll} y' = f(x, y, z) & y = b \\ z' = g(x, y, z) & z = c \end{array} \right\} \quad \text{for } x = a,$$

where f and g are continuous and satisfy Lipschitz conditions in y and z. At the nth step we define the pair of functions

$$y_n(x) = b + \int_a^x f\{t, y_{n-1}(t), z_{n-1}(t)\} dt,$$

$$z_n(x) = c + \int_a^x g\{t, y_{n-1}(t), z_{n-1}(t)\} dt,$$

and use induction to show that $y_n(x)$ and $z_n(x)$ tend to limits which give the solution required. We shall see in § 5 that an equation of order n is equivalent to a system of n equations of the first order, and so the above extension yields an existence theorem for equations of order n.

Examples.

1. Show that, if $m = -\dfrac{4k}{2k+1}$, the equation

$$y' + y^2 = ax^m$$

can be reduced to one of similar form in which $m = -\dfrac{4k}{2k-1}$ by putting $x^{m+1} = X$, $(m+1)y = a/Y$; and show that the new equation can be reduced to one of the old form with $k-1$ in place of k by putting $X = \dfrac{1}{\xi}$, $Y = \dfrac{1}{X} - \dfrac{\eta}{X^2}$.

Solve the equation

$$y' + y^2 = x^{-4/3}.$$

2. Show that, if y_0 is any particular integral of

(1) $$y' = p(x)y^2 + q(x)y + r(x),$$

then the function $1/(y - y_0)$ satisfies a linear differential equation of the first order.

Show that the cross-ratio of any four given particular integrals of (1) is independent of x.

Verify that $\cot x$ is a solution of the equation

$$2y' + y^2 \sec^2 x - y \sec x \operatorname{cosec} x + 2 \operatorname{cosec}^2 x = 0,$$

and find the general solution.

3. If $f(x) \to l$ as $x \to \infty$, prove that, if $a > 0$, every solution of the equation

$$y' + ay = f(x)$$

tends to the limit l/a as $x \to \infty$. If, however, $a < 0$, only one solution tends to l/a.

4. Sketch the solutions of each of the equations

$$\text{(a)} \quad y' + y = \frac{1}{x}, \qquad \text{(b)} \quad y' - y = \frac{1}{x}.$$

5. Sketch the solutions of each of the equations

$$\text{(a)} \quad y' = x^2 + y^2 - 1, \qquad \text{(b)} \quad y' = \frac{1}{1 - x^2 - y^2}.$$

What relation is there between the two sets of curves?

6. Verify that the process of successive approximation of § 3 applied to the equation $y' = ky$ yields the known solution. Carry out the same verification for the pair of simultaneous equations

$$y' = z, \quad z' = -y \qquad (y = 0, \ z = 1, \text{ when } x = 0).$$

7. Find the solution, for $x \geqq 0$, of the equation

$$y' = \max(x, y), \qquad y(0) = 0.$$

8. Find the solutions, as far as the terms in x^5, of the equations

(i) $y' = x^2 + \sin y,$ $y(0) = 0;$
(ii) $y' = xz,$ $y(0) = 0,$
     $z' = x + y,$ $z(0) = 1.$

9. Discuss the behaviour near the origin of solutions of the equation

$$y' = \frac{ax + by}{lx + my} \qquad (am - bl \neq 0),$$

distinguishing the cases $(b - l)^2 + 4am > 0, \ = 0$ or < 0.

10. Define $f(x, y)$ so that the equation $y' = f(x, y)$ shall have solutions

$$\begin{aligned}
&y = Ax^2 \text{ for } -1 \leqq A \leqq 1 && \text{if } |y| \leqq x^2, \\
&y = x^2 + B \text{ for } B > 0 && \text{if } y > x^2, \\
&y = -x^2 - B && \text{if } y < -x^2.
\end{aligned}$$

Prove that $f(x, y)$ is continuous at $(0, 0)$.

11. $R_1(x)$, $R_2(x)$ are continuous, and $R_1 > R_2$, in $0 \leqq x \leqq a$, and $F(x, y)$ is continuous in (x, y) for $0 \leqq x \leqq a$ and all y. Given that y_1, y_2 are solutions in $0 \leqq x \leqq a$ of

$$y' = F(x, y) + R_1(x), \qquad y' = F(x, y) + R_2(x)$$

respectively with $y_1(0) \geqq y_2(0)$, prove that $y_1 > y_2$ in $0 < x \leqq a$.
Show that the equation

$$y' = 1 + y^2 + x^2 \qquad (x \geqq 0), \qquad y(0) = 0$$

has a solution with a vertical asymptote $x = x_0$, where $x_0 \leqq \frac{1}{2}\pi$.

CHAPTER II

THE LINEAR EQUATION

5. Existence theorem. Our next task is to obtain an existence theorem for solutions of the nth order equation

$$y^{(n)} = f(x, y, y', \ldots, y^{(n-1)}),$$

where $y^{(n)}$ denotes the nth derivative of y.

Suppose that, for a value ξ of x, the values of $y, y', \ldots, y^{(n-1)}$ are given to be $\eta, \eta_1, \ldots, \eta_{n-1}$ respectively. What conditions on f are sufficient to ensure the existence of a unique solution of the equation in an interval containing ξ? As we have already remarked on page 9 this problem can be reduced to that of n first-order equations with x as independent variable and n dependent variables which we shall call $y_0, y_1, \ldots, y_{n-1}$.

The system of equations

$$y_0' = y_1,$$
$$y_1' = y_2,$$
$$\cdot \quad \cdot \quad \cdot \quad \cdot \quad \cdot$$
$$y_{n-2}' = y_{n-1},$$
$$y_{n-1}' = f(x, y_0, y_1, \ldots, y_{n-1}),$$

with the initial conditions that $y_0 = \eta$, $y_1 = \eta_1, \ldots,$ $y_{n-1} = \eta_{n-1}$ for $x = \xi$ is equivalent to the given nth order equation.

The work on page 9 then yields the following existence theorem.

THEOREM 3. *If $f(x, y, y', \ldots, y^{(n-1)})$ is a continuous function of its $n + 1$ variables in a given $n + 1$ dimensional domain D and satisfies a Lipschitz condition in each of*

$y, y', \ldots, y^{(n-1)}$, *then there is an interval of x including ξ in which the equation*

$$y^{(n)} = f(x, y, y', \ldots, y^{(n-1)})$$

has a unique solution for which

$$y = \eta, \ y' = \eta_1, \ldots, y^{(n-1)} = \eta_{n-1}$$

at $x = \xi$, *where* $(\xi, \eta, \eta_1, \ldots \eta_{n-1})$ *is a point of* D.

6. The linear equation. The general equation of order n linear in y and its derivatives is

$$p_0(x)y^{(n)} + p_1(x)y^{(n-1)} + \ldots + p_n(x)y = r(x).$$

We shall write the left-hand side as $L(y)$, L being the differential operator $p_0 D^n + \ldots + p_n$. We shall assume throughout this chapter that the p's are continuous functions of x for $a \leqq x \leqq b$, and that $p_0(x)$ does not vanish for any such x. Then the existence theorem of § 5 in the form indicated by the Corollary on page 8 shows that there is a unique solution $y = y(x)$ for $a \leqq x \leqq b$ for which $y, y', \ldots, y^{(n-1)}$ take assigned values for a given value of x.

If $r(x) \equiv 0$ for $a \leqq x \leqq b$, the equation

$$L(y) = p_0(x)y^{(n)} + \ldots + p_n(x)y = 0 \qquad (H)$$

is **homogeneous.** Otherwise the equation is non-homogeneous and will be referred to as (N). The methods of solution of these equations depend on two principles.[†]

(i) If $u_1, \ldots, u_m$ are solutions of (H), then, for any constants c_i, $c_1 u_1 + \ldots + c_m u_m$ is a solution of (H).

(ii) If u is a solution of (H) and v is a solution of (N), then $u + v$ is a solution of (N).

We discuss first the equation (H).

7. Independent solutions. A set of functions $u_1(x), \ldots, u_n(x)$ is said to be **linearly dependent** in (a, b) if there

† Ince, Text, § 37.

are constants $c_1, \ldots, c_n$, not all zero, such that

$$c_1 u_1 + \ldots + c_n u_n \equiv 0 \text{ for } a \leqq x \leqq b.$$

Otherwise the functions are linearly independent.

A useful criterion for linear independence or dependence will be given presently. It involves the Wronskian determinant [†]

$$W = W(u_1, \ldots, u_n) = \begin{vmatrix} u_1 & u_2 & \ldots & u_n \\ u_1' & u_2' & \ldots & u_n' \\ \ldots & \ldots & \ldots & \ldots \\ u_1^{(n-1)} & u_2^{(n-1)} & \ldots & u_n^{(n-1)} \end{vmatrix}$$

THEOREM 4. *The equation* (H) *has not more than n linearly independent solutions.*

PROOF. Suppose that $u_1, \ldots, u_m$ are solutions of (H), where $m > n$.

Let ξ be any point of (a, b). The n equations

$$c_1 u_1(\xi) + \ldots + c_m u_m(\xi) = 0$$
$$\ldots \ldots \ldots \ldots \ldots \ldots \ldots \ldots \ldots \ldots$$
$$c_1 u_1^{(n-1)}(\xi) + \ldots + c_m u_m^{(n-1)}(\xi) = 0,$$

in m unknowns $c_1, \ldots, c_m$ have a solution other than $c_1 = \ldots = c_m = 0$.[*] Choosing such a non-trivial solution, write

$$v(x) = c_1 u_1(x) + \ldots + c_m u_m(x).$$

Then $v(x)$ satisfies (H), and the above n equations give

$$v(\xi) = v'(\xi) = \ldots = v^{(n-1)}(\xi) = 0.$$

But $y = 0$ satisfies (H) and vanishes with all its derivatives at ξ. By the uniqueness theorem, $v(x) = 0$ for $a \leqq x \leqq b$, that is to say, there is a linear relation connecting $u_1, \ldots u_m$.

THEOREM 5. *A necessary condition that a set of n functions* $u_1, \ldots, u_n$, *having derivatives of order* $n - 1$, *are linearly dependent in* (a, b) *is that* $W \equiv 0$.

[†] Aitken, *Determinants and Matrices*, p. 132.
[*] Aitken, p. 63.

PROOF. There is a linear relation, true for all x in (a, b),

$$c_1u_1 + \ldots + c_nu_n = 0.$$

Differentiate $(n - 1)$ times. The set of n equations so obtained is satisfied by a set of c's not all zero. Therefore $W = 0$ for all x in (a, b) and the theorem is proved.

Observe that the condition $W \equiv 0$ is not sufficient for the existence of a linear relation connecting a set of differentiable functions throughout the interval. For consider

$$u_1 = x^2, \quad u_2 = 0, \quad x \geqq 0,$$
$$u_1 = 0, \quad u_2 = x^2, \quad x < 0.$$

$W = 0$ for all values of x, but there is no linear relation connecting u_1 and u_2 in an interval including the origin. In fact two different linear relations $u_1 = 0$ and $u_2 = 0$ hold for negative and positive x respectively.

If, however, the functions are known to be solutions of a linear differential equation, the next theorem shows that $W = 0$ *is* a sufficient condition for linear dependence.

THEOREM 6. *If* $u_1, \ldots, u_n$ *are solutions of* (H), *and* $W(\xi) = 0$ *where* $a \leqq \xi \leqq b$, *then the* u_i *are linearly dependent, and so* $W(x) = 0$ *for all* x *in* (a, b).

PROOF. The equations

$$c_1u_1(\xi) + \ldots + c_nu_n(\xi) = 0,$$
$$\cdot \ \cdot \ \cdot \ \cdot \ \cdot \ \cdot \ \cdot \ \cdot \ \cdot \ \cdot \ \cdot$$
$$c_1u_1^{(n-1)}(\xi) + \ldots + c_nu_n^{(n-1)}(\xi) = 0,$$

having a vanishing determinant, have a set of solutions $c_1, \ldots, c_n$, not all zero. Write

$$v = c_1u_1 + \ldots + c_nu_n$$

and argue as in theorem 4. We have $v \equiv 0$ and the theorem follows.

We observe that the Wronskian of a set of n solutions of an equation (H) either vanishes identically or does not vanish at all.

A set of n linearly independent solutions of (H) is called a **fundamental set.**

THEOREM 7. *The equation (H) possesses a fundamental set of solutions, $u_1, u_2, \ldots, u_n$, say, and its general solution is then*

$$y = C_1 u_1 + C_2 u_2 + \ldots + C_n u_n,$$

where $C_1, C_2, \ldots C_n$ are arbitrary constants.

PROOF. Choose numbers $a_{ij}(i = 1, \ldots, n; j = 1, \ldots, n)$ with the sole restriction that their determinant does not vanish. For each j, there exists a solution $u_j(x)$ such that the values of u_j and its first $n - 1$ derivatives at the point $x = \xi$ are respectively $a_{1j}, a_{2j}, \ldots, a_{nj}$. A simple choice of a_{ij} would be $a_{ii} = 1$, $a_{ij} = 0$ $(i \neq j)$.

By theorem 5 the functions u_j are linearly independent, and by theorem 4, every solution is of the form

$$y = C_1 u_1 + \ldots + C_n u_n.$$

THEOREM 8. (*Liouville's formula*).

If $W(x) = W(u_1, u_2, \ldots, u_n)$ is the Wronskian of n solutions of the equation (H),

$$p_0(x)y^{(n)} + \ldots + p_n(x)y = 0,$$

then

$$W(x) = W(\xi)\, exp\left\{ - \int_\xi^x \frac{p_1(t)}{p_0(t)}\, dt \right\}.$$

PROOF. $W'(x)$ is the sum of n determinants,

$$\Delta_1 + \Delta_2 + \ldots + \Delta_n$$

say, where Δ_r is got from W by differentiating the rth row and leaving the others unchanged. Each Δ_r except Δ_n has two rows identical and is zero. Hence

$$W' = \begin{vmatrix} u_1 & u_2 & \ldots & u_n \\ \cdots & \cdots & \cdots & \cdots \\ u_1^{(n-2)} & u_2^{(n-2)} & \ldots & u_n^{(n-2)} \\ u_1^{(n)} & u_2^{(n)} & \ldots & u_n^{(n)} \end{vmatrix}.$$

In the last row, substitute for each $u^{(n)}$ from the equation

$$p_0 u^{(n)} = -p_1 u^{(n-1)} - \ldots - p_n u$$

and again omit vanishing determinants. This gives

$$p_0(x) W'(x) = -p_1(x) W(x).$$

Integrating this equation, we have the theorem.

8. Solution of non-homogeneous equation. If a fundamental set of solutions of the homogeneous equation has been found, the equation

$$L(y) = r(x) \tag{N}$$

can be solved by Lagrange's method of **variation of parameters.**

Let $u_1, \ldots, u_n$ be n independent solutions of (H). Write

$$y = V_1 u_1 + \ldots + V_n u_n,$$

where the V's, instead of being constants, will be functions of x.

$$y' = V_1 u_1' + \ldots + V_n u_n' + [V_1' u_1 + \ldots + V_n' u_n].$$

The V's will be chosen to make the sum of the terms within square brackets vanish for all x.

Continuing, we have

$$y'' = V_1 u_1'' + \ldots + V_n u_n'' + [V_1' u_1' + \ldots + V_n' u_n'].$$

Again make the sum of the terms in square brackets zero. Repeat this process up to $y^{(n-1)}$. Finally,

$$y^{(n)} = V_1 u_1^{(n)} + \ldots + V_n u_n^{(n)} + [V_1' u_1^{(n-1)} + \ldots + V_n' u_n^{(n-1)}].$$

Make the sum of the terms in these square brackets equal to $r(x)/p_0(x)$.

Multiplying the expressions for $y^{(n)}, \ldots, y', y$ by $p_0, \ldots, p_{n-1}, p_n$ respectively and adding, we see that y satisfies (N).

The values assigned to the square brackets provide n equations for $V_1', \ldots, V_n'$. The determinant of the coefficients is the Wronskian of the u's and is consequently not zero. Thus, the n equations for V_i' have the solution $V_i' = W_i/W$, where W_i is got from W by replacing the ith column by $(0, 0, \ldots, 0, r/p_0)$.

The solution of (N) is then

$$y = u_1 \int \frac{W_1}{W} \, dx + \ldots + u_n \int \frac{W_n}{W} \, dx,$$

and so is obtainable by quadratures (i.e. the evaluation of integrals) from the solution of (H).

9. Second-order linear equation. We turn to possible methods of solving the general linear equation. From § 8, it is sufficient to discuss (H). One important case is well-known; if the coefficients are constants, the solution of the differential equation is found when we have solved the corresponding algebraic equation (Ince, Text, Chap. V).

For the general linear equation, there are as a rule no solutions obtainable in finite terms. If such solutions do exist, they are usually revealed by one of the devices mentioned below. For brevity the discussion is restricted to the second-order equation, and, dividing the equation by $p_0(x)$, we take the coefficient of y'' to be 1.

Reduction of order. In the equation

$$y'' + p_1 y' + p_2 y = 0,$$

write $y = uv$, where u and v are functions of x, and arrange the result as an equation for v,

$$uv'' + (2u' + p_1 u)v' + (u'' + p_1 u' + p_2 u)v = 0.$$

If any particular solution u of the original equation is known, the coefficient of v in the equation for v vanishes and we are left with a linear equation for v', and so a value of v containing two arbitrary constants can be found by quadratures.

The same method shows that a knowledge of a solution of the nth order equation reduces the problem to an equation of order $n - 1$.

Normal form of the second-order equation. In the last equation choose u to make

$$2u' + p_1u = 0,$$

from which we have

$$u = \exp\{-\tfrac{1}{2}\int p_1dx\}.$$

Then the equation for v becomes

$$v'' + Iv = 0,$$

where
$$I = p_2 - \tfrac{1}{2}p_1' - \tfrac{1}{4}p_1^2.$$

This equation, containing no term in v', is said to be in **normal form.** A second-order equation in normal form usually gives the best chance of finding a solution by inspection.

Factorization of operator. This method is rather artificial, but it is elegant when applicable. Writing D for d/dx, we try to express

$$(D^2 + p_1D + p_2)y = 0$$
as
$$(D + u)(D + v)y = 0,$$

where u and v are functions of x (different of course from those of the last section). Observe that the operators $D + u$ and $D + v$ do not commute. If the factorization is effected, the second-order equation is reduced to two linear first-order equations

$$(D + u)z = 0, \quad (D + v)y = z,$$

which can be solved.

Since $(D+u)(D+v)y = D^2y + (u+v)Dy + (uv+v')y$, we have by comparison with the original equation

$$u + v = p_1,$$
$$uv + v' = p_2.$$

The equation for v is then

$$v' + vp_1 - v^2 = p_2,$$

which, being of Riccati's type, is not in general soluble in finite terms, even for an equation in normal form with $p_1 = 0$.

10. Adjoint equations. It is natural to ask whether a search for an *integrating factor* will help towards solving the second-order equation. Taking

$$L(y) \equiv p_0 y'' + p_1 y' + p_2 y,$$

can we find a function z of x such that

$$zL(y) = \frac{d}{dx} L_1(y),$$

where $L_1(y)$ is a differential operator of the first order? Integrating by parts, we have

$$\int zL(y)dx = p_0 zy' - (p_0 z)'y + \int (p_0 z)''y\, dx$$
$$+ p_1 zy - \int (p_1 z)'y\, dx$$
$$+ \int p_2 zy\, dx.$$

The integrals on the right-hand side vanish, making $zL(y)$ an exact differential if z satisfies

$$M(z) \equiv (p_0 z)'' - (p_1 z)' + p_2 z = 0.$$

So the finding of an integrating factor involves the solution of another second-order equation and we are generally no better off.

The operator M is called the **adjoint** of L. From the above argument, we have **Lagrange's identity**

$$zL(y) - yM(z) = \frac{d}{dx} \{p_0(y'z - yz') + (p_1 - p_0')yz\}.$$

It is easy to verify that the relation of being adjoint is reciprocal; L is the adjoint of M. If L, M are the same, the equation is **self-adjoint.** The necessary and sufficient condition for this is that $p_1 = p_0'$, and the equation in this case is

$$\frac{d}{dx}\left(p_0 \frac{dy}{dx}\right) + p_2 y = 0,$$

and Lagrange's identity reduces to

$$zL(y) - yL(z) = \frac{d}{dx}\{p_0(y'z - yz')\}.$$

Some of the most common equations of mathematical physics are of the self-adjoint form. For example, the equation of Legendre, discussed in Chapter VII, is self-adjoint.

Examples.

Solve the equations 1—8.

1. $y'''' - y = \cos x$.

2. $y''' - 3y' + 2y = 3e^x$.

3. $(ax + 1)^2 y'' + a(ax + 1)y' + b^2 y = 0$.

4. $(1 - x)y'' + xy' - y = (1 - x)^2$.

5. $(1 + x^2)y'' + xy' = 4y$.

6. $y''(\frac{1}{2}x^2 - x) + y'(-\frac{1}{2}x^2 + 1) + y(x - 1) = 0$.

7. $x^2 y'' - x(x + 2)y' + (x + 2)y = x^3$.

8. $(x^2 - 1)y'' - 2xy' + 2y = (x^2 - 1)^2$.

9. Find the solution of the simultaneous differential equations

$$-\frac{dx}{dt} + \frac{dy}{dt} + \frac{dz}{dt} - x + 2z = e^{-t}$$

$$\frac{dx}{dt} - \frac{dy}{dt} + \frac{dz}{dt} + x \qquad = 2e^{-t}$$

$$\frac{dx}{dt} + \frac{dy}{dt} - \frac{dz}{dt} + x + 2y = 3e^{-t}$$

if $x = x_0$, $y = y_0$, $z = z_0$ at $t = 0$.

If x, y, z are the coordinates of a moving point P, prove that P approaches the origin O as $t \to \infty$. In what direction does P enter O?

10. Prove that, if

$$\ddot{x} + ax + hy = 0$$
$$\ddot{y} + hx + by = 0,$$

where $a > 0$, $b > 0$, $ab > h^2$, and dots denote differentiation with respect to t, then

$$\dot{x}^2 + \dot{y}^2 + V = C,$$

where $V = ax^2 + 2hxy + by^2$.

Hence find upper bounds to the magnitudes of x, y, $\dot{x}$, $\dot{y}$ in terms of the constant C.

11. Verify that $y = e^{ix^2}$ satisfies the equation

$$xy'' - y' + 4x^3 y = 0,$$

and deduce the general solution.

12. Given that the equation

$$L(y) \equiv y'' + p_1(x)y' + p_2(x)y = 0$$

has solutions $y = \cos x$ and $y = \tan x$, find the general solution of the equation

$$L(y) = \frac{\cos x}{1 + \sin^2 x}.$$

13. If

$$\frac{d^2y}{dx^2} + Q(x)\frac{dy}{dx} + R(x)y \equiv \left(\frac{d}{dx} - u(x)\right)\left(\frac{d}{dx} - v(x)\right)y,$$

find a first-order differential equation, not involving v, satisfied by u.

Apply this to the equation

$$\frac{d^2y}{dx^2} - \tan x\,\frac{dy}{dx} - \frac{2}{1 + \sin x}\,y = 0;$$

using the substitution $u \cos x = z$, or otherwise, find a solution for u and hence solve completely the given equation.

14. Show that, if $f(x)$ is continuous for $x \geqq 1$, then the solution of the equation

$$xy''' - y'' + xy' - y = f(x)$$

that is valid for $x \geqq 1$ and is such that $y'' = y' = y = 0$ when $x = 1$ may be written in the form

$$y = \int_1^x f(t)g(x, t)dt,$$

and determine the function $g(x, t)$.

15. Show that a necessary and sufficient condition for the expression

$$P(x)\frac{d^2y}{dx^2} + Q(x)\frac{dy}{dx} + R(x)y$$

to be expressible in the form

$$\frac{d}{dx}\left\{ L(x)\frac{dy}{dx} + M(x)y \right\}$$

is that

$$P''(x) - Q'(x) + R(x) \equiv 0.$$

Solve completely the differential equation

$$x(1 + x)\frac{d^2y}{dx^2} - \{n + (n - 2)x\}\frac{dy}{dx} - ny = x^{n+1}.$$

16. Prove that the differential equation

$$xy'' + 2ny' + kxy = 0,$$

where n is a positive integer and k a real constant, is satisfied by

$$y = \left(\frac{1}{x}\frac{d}{dx}\right)^n u,$$

where u is a solution of the equation

$$u'' + ku = 0.$$

Find the solution of the differential equation

$$xy'' + 4y' + xy = 0$$

for which $y = 0$ and $y' = 1$ when $x = \pi$; prove that, when $x = 2\pi$, $y = 1/(8\pi)$.

17. Let $u_1(x), \ldots, u_n(x)$ be continuous in (a, b). Write

$$a_{ij} = \int_a^b u_i(x)u_j(x)dx \qquad (1 \leqq i, j \leqq n).$$

Let G be the determinant of order n (the Gramian) whose elements are a_{ij}. Prove that $G = 0$ is a necessary and sufficient condition for the linear dependence of $u_1(x), \ldots, u_n(x)$ in (a, b).

18. If $c_1u_1(x) + c_2u_2(x)$ is the general solution of the equation $y'' + p_1y' + p_2y = 0$, obtain the general solution of the adjoint equation.

19. Solve the equation

$$(x + 1)x^2y'' + xy' - (x + 1)^3y = 0,$$

given that there are two solutions whose product is a constant.

(This example illustrates the principle that a given fact about solutions, holding throughout an interval of values of x, can often be used to reduce by one the order of the differential equation).

20. If the equation $y'' + p_1y' + p_2y = 0$ has two solutions whose product is a constant, find the relation between p_1 and p_2.

CHAPTER III

OSCILLATION THEOREMS

11. Convexity of solutions. The theorems of this chapter show that, although we cannot in general obtain explicit solutions of second-order equations, a good deal can be said about their behaviour. Theorems like 12 and 13, which deal with zeros of solutions, their distance apart etc., are typical and give the title to the chapter.

Consider the homogeneous equation in normal form

$$y'' + g(x)y = 0,$$

where $g(x)$ is continuous. The key-note of theorems 9 and 10 is that the sign of y'' determines whether the curve $y = y(x)$ is convex or concave.

THEOREM 9. *If $g(x) < 0$ in the interval (a, b), then any solution $u(x)$ (not identically 0) of the equation $y'' + g(x)y = 0$ has at most one zero in (a, b).*

PROOF. Suppose that $u(x_0) = 0$. Then $u'(x_0) \neq 0$, for if $u'(x_0) = 0$ then $u(x) \equiv 0$ by the uniqueness theorem. If $u'(x_0) > 0$, then there is an interval to the right of x_0 in which $u(x)$ is positive and so, for $x > x_0$, the function $u''(x) = - g(x)u(x)$ is positive; hence $u'(x)$ is an increasing function. Therefore $u(x)$ has no zero to the right of x_0, and similarly none to the left. A like argument holds if $u'(x_0) < 0$. So $u(x)$ has one zero or none in (a, b).

To obtain further results we take account of the magnitude of $g(x)$. It will be helpful to compare two equations

$$y'' + g(x)y = 0, \quad (Y)$$
$$z'' + h(x)z = 0. \quad (Z)$$

THEOREM 10. *Let* $g(x) < h(x)$ *for* $x \geqq x_0$. *Let* $y(x)$ *be the solution of* (Y) *with the initial conditions* $y(x_0) = y_0$, $y'(x_0) = y_0'$, *these conditions being such that* $y(x) > 0$ *for some interval to the right of* x_0. *Let* $z(x)$ *be the solution of* (Z) *satisfying the conditions* $z(x_0) = y_0$, $z'(x_0) = y_0'$. *Then* $y(x) > z(x)$ *for* $x > x_0$, *so long as* $z(x) > 0$.

PROOF. (Y) and (Z) give

$$y''z - yz'' = (h - g)yz.$$

Integrating from x_0 to x, we have

$$y'z - yz' = \int_{x_0}^{x} (h - g)yz\,dx.$$

The right-hand side is positive so long as y and z are. Since $\dfrac{d}{dx}\left(\dfrac{y}{z}\right) = \dfrac{y'z - yz'}{z^2} > 0$, $\dfrac{y}{z}$ is an increasing function. But, for $x = x_0$, y/z is 1 if $y_0 \neq 0$ or tends to 1 if $y_0 = 0$. The theorem follows.

COROLLARY 1. *If* $y(\xi) = 0$ *for some* $\xi > x_0$, *then* $z(\eta) = 0$ *for some* η *between* x_0 *and* ξ.

COROLLARY 2. *If the values of* $y(x_0)$, $y'(x_0)$ *are such that* $y(x) < 0$ *for an interval to the right of* x_0, *then the conclusion is that* $y(x) < z(x)$ *so long as* $z(x) < 0$. *Both cases are included in the statement* $|y(x)| > |z(x)|$ *for* $x > x_0$, *so long as* $z(x)$ *does not vanish.*

The following calculation illustrates the use of a comparison differential equation for estimates of magnitude of solutions.

If, in (Y), *as* $x \to \infty$, $g(x) \to -a^2 (a > 0)$, *then, for arbitrarily small positive* η, *any positive solution of* (Y) *satisfies the inequalities*

$$e^{(a-\eta)x} < y(x) < e^{(a+\eta)x}$$

for all sufficiently large positive x.

Take x_0 large enough to make

$$(a - \tfrac{1}{2}\eta)^2 < -g(x) < (a + \tfrac{1}{2}\eta)^2 \text{ for } x \geqq x_0.$$

Taking $b = a - \frac{1}{2}\eta$, construct the solution of $z'' - b^2 z = 0$ with $z(x_0) = y(x_0)$, $z'(x_0) = y'(x_0)$. This is

$$Ae^{bx} + Be^{-bx},$$

where A and B depend on y_0, y_0'. By theorem 10,

$$y(x) > Ae^{bx} + Be^{-bx}$$
$$> e^{(a-\eta)x} \text{ for all sufficiently large } x.$$

The other inequality is proved similarly.

12. Zeros of solutions. If (Y) has a solution (not identically 0) with more than one zero, theorem 9 shows that there must be an interval in which $g(x) > 0$.

THEOREM 11. *A finite value ξ cannot be a limit point of zeros of a solution $u(x)$ of (Y), unless $u(x) \equiv 0$.*

PROOF. Suppose $\xi = \lim x_n$, where $u(x_n) = 0$. Since $u(x)$ is continuous, $u(\xi) = 0$. Also

$$u'(\xi) = \lim_{x_n \to \xi} \frac{u(x_n) - u(\xi)}{x_n - \xi} = 0.$$

By the uniqueness theorem, $u(x) \equiv 0$.

THEOREM 12. *The zeros of two linearly independent solutions of (Y) interlace i.e. between two consecutive zeros of one lies a zero of the other.*

PROOF. Observe that, if two solutions both vanish at a point, their Wronskian is 0 and they are linearly dependent (i.e. one is a constant multiple of the other).

Suppose that $u_1(x)$, $u_2(x)$ are linearly independent solutions of (Y), and that α, β are consecutive zeros of $u_1(x)$.

From $u_1'' + g u_1 = 0$, $u_2'' + g u_2 = 0$, we have

$$u_1'' u_2 - u_1 u_2'' = 0.$$

Integrate from α to β and we have

$$\left[u_1' u_2 - u_1 u_2' \right]_\alpha^\beta = 0.$$

Hence $\qquad u_1'(\beta)u_2(\beta) = u_1'(\alpha)u_2(\alpha).$

Since α, β are consecutive zeros of $u_1(x)$, $u_1'(\alpha)$ and $u_1'(\beta)$ have opposite signs. Therefore $u_2(\alpha)$ and $u_2(\beta)$ have opposite signs, and so $u_2(x)$ vanishes at least once between α and β. Interchanging the rôles of u_1 and u_2, we see that their zeros interlace.

THEOREM 13.

If $0 < m < g(x) < M$ for $a \leqq x \leqq b$,

and, if x_0, x_1 are consecutive zeros (lying in (a, b)) of a solution of (Y), then

$$\frac{\pi}{\sqrt{M}} < x_1 - x_0 < \frac{\pi}{\sqrt{m}}.$$

PROOF. Refer to theorem 10 and its corollaries, and compare with the equation $z'' + Mz = 0$. The solution of this equation which vanishes at x_0 and has $z_0' = y_0'$ is

$$z = \frac{y_0'}{\sqrt{M}} \sin (x - x_0)\sqrt{M}.$$

Since the next zero of z is at $x_0 + \dfrac{\pi}{\sqrt{M}}$, we have

$$x_1 - x_0 > \frac{\pi}{\sqrt{M}}.$$

A similar proof gives the other inequality.

COROLLARY. *The number n of zeros within the interval (x_0, x) satisfies*

$$\frac{x - x_0}{\pi} \sqrt{m} < n < \frac{x - x_0}{\pi} \sqrt{M}.$$

Referring again to theorem 10, its corollaries state that the first zero of $z(x)$ greater than x_0 is to the left of the first zero of $y(x)$. We now prove by induction that if there are further zeros, the nth zero ζ_n of $z(x)$ is to the left of the nth zero η_n of $y(x)$. Suppose that $\zeta_{n-1} < \eta_{n-1}$. Let

$y_1(x)$ be the solution of (Y) which vanishes at ζ_{n-1} and has the same gradient there as $z(x)$. By theorem 10, ζ_n is to the left of the next zero of $y_1(x)$. By theorem 12, $y_1(x)$ has a zero between η_{n-1} and η_n. Therefore $\zeta_n < \eta_n$, completing the induction.

13. Eigenvalues. To lead up to the general theorem which follows, consider the equation with constant coefficients

$$y'' + \lambda y = 0,$$

and seek a solution such that $y(0) = y(\pi) = 0$. The general solution of the equation is

$$y = A \sin \sqrt{\lambda} x + B \cos \sqrt{\lambda} x$$

and (assuming that y is not identically 0) the conditions at 0 and π can be satisfied only if λ has one of the values $1^2,\ 2^2, \ldots,\ n^2, \ldots$

These values of λ are called **eigenvalues** (the hybrid coming from the German translation *Eigenwert* of *characteristic value*).

The corresponding solutions, namely $\sin nx (n = 1, 2, \ldots)$ are called **eigenfunctions**; they have the property of orthogonality i.e.

$$\int_0^\pi \sin mx \sin nx\, dx = 0, \quad (m \neq n).$$

and a function $f(x)$, for which $f(0) = f(\pi) = 0$, if sufficiently well-behaved, can be expanded as a Fourier series of multiples of $\sin nx$ in the form

$$f(x) = \sum_1^\infty b_n \sin nx, \qquad (0 \leqq x \leqq \pi).$$

THEOREM 14. *Let $g(x) > 0$ in (a, b). Let $y_\lambda(x)$ be the solution of the equation.*

$$y'' + \lambda g(x) y = 0$$

for which $y_\lambda(a) = 0$, $y'_\lambda(a) = k(\neq 0)$. Then $y_\lambda(b) = 0$ if and only if λ has one of an infinite sequence of values $\lambda_1, \lambda_2, \ldots$ tending to $+ \infty$.

PROOF. We shall first prove that any particular zero (say the mth) of $y_\lambda(x)$ is a continuous function of λ. Let us prove this for $\lambda = \alpha$. Enclose the mth zero $\eta_m(\alpha)$ in an interval (c, d) containing no other zero of $y_\alpha(x)$. Then $y_\alpha(c)$ and $y_\alpha(d)$ have opposite signs. Now appeal to the property stated on page 9 of continuous dependence of solutions on the parameter λ. This ensures that, for all λ sufficiently near to α, $y_\lambda(c)$ and $y_\lambda(d)$ have opposite signs, and so $y_\lambda(x)$ has a zero in (c, d). Since (c, d) is arbitrarily small, this shows that a given zero is a continuous function of λ.

From the last paragraph of § 12, $\eta_m(\lambda)$ decreases as λ increases. Let λ take values increasing from $- \infty$ to $+ \infty$. For $\lambda < 0$, by theorem 9, $y_\lambda(x)$ has no zero other than a. As $\lambda \to \infty$, by theorem 13 (corollary), the number of zeros of $y_\lambda(x)$ in (a, b) tends to infinity. There are therefore infinitely many values of λ $(\lambda_1 < \lambda_2 < \ldots)$ for which another zero 'comes into the interval' at b. The function $y_\lambda(x)$ for $\lambda = \lambda_n$ has zeros at a and b and $(n - 1)$ zeros inside the interval (a, b).

COROLLARY 1. *If $m \leqq g(x) \leqq M$, then*

$$\frac{n^2\pi^2}{(b - a)^2 M} \leqq \lambda_n \leqq \frac{n^2\pi^2}{(b - a)^2 m}.$$

This follows from theorem 13 (corollary).

COROLLARY 2. *The argument of the theorem can be extended to the more general (self-adjoint) equation — the Sturm-Liouville equation*

$$\frac{d}{dx}\left\{p(x)\frac{dy}{dx}\right\} + \{q(x) + \lambda g(x)\}y = 0,$$

where $p(x) > 0$, $g(x) > 0$.

The change of independent variable

$$\xi = \int_a^x \frac{dt}{p(t)}$$

transforms the equation into

$$\frac{d^2y}{d\xi^2} + \{q_1(\xi) + \lambda g_1(\xi)\}y = 0,$$

to which the methods of the theorem apply.

14. Eigenfunctions and expansions.

From the extension of theorem 14 given in corollary 2 we have for the Sturm-Liouville equation a sequence of eigenvalues $\lambda_1, \lambda_2, \ldots, \lambda_n, \ldots$, and corresponding to λ_n a solution $u_n(x)$, determined except for a constant multiplier, which vanishes at a and b and at $n - 1$ points inside (a, b). This is called the nth eigenfunction.

We have

$$(pu'_m)' + (q + \lambda_m g)u_m = 0,$$
$$(pu'_n)' + (q + \lambda_n g)u_n = 0.$$

Multiply these equations by u_n and u_m, subtract, and integrate from a to b. This gives

$$\left[p(u'_m u_n - u_m u'_n) \right]_a^b + (\lambda_m - \lambda_n) \int_a^b g u_m u_n dx = 0.$$

The expression in square brackets vanishes at a and b, and so, if $m \neq n$,

$$\int_a^b g u_m u_n dx = 0.$$

The functions $u_n(x)$ may be said to form an orthogonal set in (a, b) with weight function $g(x)$.

For $m = n$, we have $\int_a^b g u_n^2 dx > 0$ because the integrand is positive. The arbitrary multiplier in u_n may be chosen so as to make the value of the integral equal to 1.

THEOREM 15. *All the eigenvalues of the equation*

$$\frac{d}{dx}\left\{ p(x)\frac{dy}{dx} \right\} + \{q(x) + \lambda g(x)\}y = 0, \qquad (a \leqq x \leqq b),$$

where $p(x) > 0$, $g(x) > 0$, *are real*.

PROOF. Suppose that there is a complex eigenvalue $\lambda_\mu = \alpha + i\beta$. Then, the coefficients of the equation being real, the conjugate complex number is also an eigenvalue, say $\lambda_\nu = \alpha - i\beta$. Let the eigenfunction corresponding to λ_μ be $u_\mu = v + iw$ say. Then $u_\nu = v - iw$. By the orthogonal property

$$\int_a^b g u_\mu u_\nu dx = 0,$$

which gives

$$\int_a^b g(v^2 + w^2)dx = 0.$$

This can only be true if $v = w \equiv 0$. Thus the theorem is proved.

The eigenfunctions form a basis of expansion of an arbitrary function $f(x)$ for which $f(a) = f(b) = 0$. Suppose that

$$f(x) = c_1 u_1(x) + \ldots + c_n u_n(x) + \ldots$$

Multiply by $g(x)u_n(x)$. If the integration term-by-term from a to b is valid, we have the value of the nth coefficient:

$$c_n = \int_a^b g(x)f(x)u_n(x)dx.$$

This expansion is only formal, and the proof of its validity under suitable assumptions about $f(x)$ is beyond the scope of this book. Justification is immediate if all the $u_n(x)$ are less than a constant and the uniform convergence of the series is assumed.

Examples of the application of the theorems of this Chapter to special functions will be found in Chapter VIII (Bessel functions).

CHAPTER IV

SOLUTION IN SERIES

15. Differential equations in complex variables.
It was remarked in § 1 that few types of differential
equations can be solved by a finite number of processes
applied to elementary functions, and the work of Chapters
II and III will have further impressed this fact on the
reader. We are thus led to investigate solutions which are
expressible by infinite processes, for example, as the sum
of an infinite series of elementary functions. A type of
infinite series which suggests itself is a power series in x,

$$y = \sum_{n=0}^{\infty} c_n x^n.$$

Problems of convergence and manipulation of power
series are as readily dealt with in complex variables as in
real variables, and the question arises whether it is appropriate to widen the scope of our discussion of differential
equations and allow the variables to be complex. It is
true that in applications to mechanics or physics the reader
will have become accustomed to real variables, and it may
seem an empty striving after generality to suppose the
variables complex.

The reason why this extension is worth while is that
differential equations derive much of their importance
from the functions which are their solutions. To restrict
the variable of a function to be real is to leave out matters
of the highest interest e.g. the relation between the exponential and trigonometric functions. In fact, the equation

$$\frac{dw}{dz} = kw,$$

where the constant k can be complex, has as solutions exponential and trigonometric functions, and yields more than the real equation $y' = ky$.

The discussion of equations in complex variables provides a wide field of application of ideas such as branch-points, singularities, analytic continuation, contour integration. † Our account will be almost entirely restricted to linear differential equations, and we shall generally suppose them to be of the second order. It is such equations which define the most important functions (c.g. Legendre, Bessel).

We write z and w for the independent and dependent variables, and the equation of order n is

$$w^{(n)} = f(z, w, w', \ldots, w^{(n-1)}),$$

where w is an analytic function of z, regular except for certain singularities.

The ideas of Chapter II such as fundamental sets of solutions and the theorems based on them apply with only verbal changes to complex variables.

A reader whose main interest is in the formal process of obtaining solutions and who is content to pass lightly over the justification may concentrate his attention on § 20, thinking if he wishes in terms of real variables.

16. Ordinary and singular points. In the linear equation

$$w'' + p(z)w' + q(z)w = 0, \qquad (16.1)$$

let $p(z)$ and $q(z)$ be regular for $|z - z_0| < R$. Then the method of successive approximation set out in § 2 and applied in § 6 to the real linear equation shows that (16.1) has a unique solution $w = w(z)$, regular for $|z - z_0| < R$, for which $w(z_0)$ and $w'(z_0)$ take assigned values w_0, w_0'. An alternative method of proof will be developed in this chapter; the detail is deferred until § 17 where it is applied to a theorem rather more general than the one just stated.

† See Phillips, *Functions of a Complex Variable.*

DEFINITION. A value $z = z_0$ for which the coefficients $p(z)$ and $q(z)$ are regular is called an **ordinary point** of the differential equation. All other points are singular points or **singularities** of the equation.

If $p(z)$ and $q(z)$ are regular for all finite z, the solutions will be regular for all finite z. For R in the first paragraph can be as large as we like.

If $p(z)$ and $q(z)$ have singularities, the solutions will in general have singularities for the values of z concerned.

Example 1.

$$w'' = zw.$$

By the remark just made, solutions will be regular for all finite z, and we may assume expansions in powers of z, †

$$w = a_0 + a_1 z + \ldots + a_n z^n + \ldots$$

Substitute in the equation and equate coefficients of powers of z. Then

$$a_2 = 0,$$
$$n(n - 1)a_n = a_{n-3}, \quad n \geqq 3.$$

So $w = a_0 \left(1 + \dfrac{z^3}{2 \cdot 3} + \dfrac{z^6}{2 \cdot 3 \cdot 5 \cdot 6} + \ldots\right) + a_1 \left(z + \dfrac{z^4}{3 \cdot 4} + \dfrac{z^7}{3 \cdot 4 \cdot 6 \cdot 7} + \ldots\right),$

where a_0 and a_1 are arbitrary constants (in fact they are the values of w and w' for $z = 0$).

Example 2.

$$w' = \frac{kw}{z}.$$

This has solutions $w = Az^k$. The origin is in general a branch point (e.g. $k = \frac{1}{2}$); it may be regular ($k = 1$) or a pole ($k = -1$).

Example 3.

$$w' = \frac{w}{z^2}.$$

Solutions are $w = A \exp(-1/z)$, which have an essential singularity at $z = 0$.

We remark that the positions of singularities of solutions of a differential equation may or may not depend on the

† Phillips, p. 95.

initial conditions. In examples 2 and 3, the singularity is at $z = 0$, whatever the initial conditions, and the singularity is *fixed*. In fact, a linear equation can only have fixed singularities. The next example gives an equation with *movable* singularities.

Example 4.

$$ww' + z = 0.$$

Solutions are

$$w^2 + z^2 = A,$$

and, if $w - w_0$ for $z = z_0$, this gives

$$w = (w_0^2 + z_0^2 - z^2)^{1/2}.$$

The singularities (branch-points) of w depend on w_0, z_0, and indeed any value of z is a branch point for suitable w_0, z_0.

17. Solutions near a regular singularity. If, in the equation (16.1), $p(z)$ and $q(z)$ have singularities at z_0, the solutions will in general have singularities there. If, however, $(z - z_0)p(z)$ and $(z - z_0)^2 q(z)$ are regular, or, in other words, $p(z)$ has at most a pole of order one and $q(z)$ a pole of order two, the singularities at z_0 of the solutions will be found to be of a clearly defined kind, and z_0 will be called a **regular singularity** of the equation. We shall for brevity take $z_0 = 0$.

A simple example gives much information about the solutions near a regular singularity.

Example.

$$w'' + \frac{a}{z} w' + \frac{b}{z^2} w = 0.$$

The origin is a regular singularity. This is Euler's linear equation (Ince, Text, p. 101) and the substitution $z = e^\zeta$ reduces it to the equation with constant coefficients

$$\frac{d^2 w}{d\zeta^2} + (a - 1)\frac{dw}{d\zeta} + bw = 0.$$

The solution of this is

$$w = Ae^{\rho_1 \zeta} + Be^{\rho_2 \zeta} \qquad (\rho_1 \neq \rho_2),$$

or

$$w = (A + B\zeta)e^{\rho_1 \zeta} \qquad (\rho_1 = \rho_2),$$

where ρ_1 and ρ_2 are the roots of the quadratic

$$\rho(\rho - 1) + a\rho + b = 0.$$

So the solutions of the original equation are

$$w = Az^{\rho_1} + Bz^{\rho_2}$$

or $$w = (A + B \log z)z^{\rho_1}$$

in the respective cases of unequal and equal roots.

Thus the solutions in general are many-valued functions having branch-points at $z = 0$, and in the equal-root case, if $w_1(z)$ is the solution z^{ρ_1} immediately given by the root ρ_1, a second solution is $w_1(z) \log z$.

Formal calculation of solutions of

$$w'' + p(z)w' + q(z)w = 0,$$

where $zp(z)$ and $z^2q(z)$ are regular at $z = 0$.

There is a circle, centre $z = 0$, in which

$$zp(z) = p_0 + p_1 z + \ldots + p_n z^n + \ldots$$
$$z^2 q(z) = q_0 + q_1 z + \ldots + q_n z^n + \ldots$$

Try to solve the equation by

$$w = z^\rho(c_0 + c_1 z + \ldots + c_n z^n + \ldots) \quad (c_0 \neq 0).$$

Substitute and equate coefficients of $z^{\rho-2}, z^{\rho-1}, \ldots z^{\rho+n-2}$. We obtain

$$c_0\{\rho(\rho - 1) + \rho p_0 + q_0\} = 0,$$
$$c_1\{(\rho + 1)\rho + (\rho + 1)p_0 + q_0\} + c_0(\rho p_1 + q_1) = 0.$$

For the $(n + 1)$th equation, write for brevity

$$F(\rho) \equiv \rho(\rho - 1) + \rho p_0 + q_0,$$

and it is

$$c_n F(\rho + n) + \sum_{s=0}^{n-1} c_s\{(\rho + s)p_{n-s} + q_{n-s}\} = 0. \quad (17.1)$$

The first equation gives the quadratic for ρ

$$F(\rho) = 0.$$

This is called the **indicial equation,** and its roots, say ρ_1 and ρ_2, are the **exponents** at the value of z ($z = 0$) under consideration. The equations after the first give successively the values of $c_1, \ldots, c_n, \ldots$ in terms of c_0. The equations are linear, and, for each value of ρ, the c's are uniquely determined unless, for some value of n, the coefficient of c_n in the equation for c_n vanishes, that is to say, $F(\rho + n) = 0$. If $\rho_1 - \rho_2 = n$, then $\rho = \rho_1$ gives a (formal) solution, but $F(\rho_2 + n) = 0$ and the process does not, in general, give a solution for $\rho = \rho_2$. Moreover, if $\rho_1 = \rho_2$, we obtain only one solution. Leaving aside until § 19 the further investigation required when the indicial equation has equal roots or roots differing by an integer, we establish the convergence of the power series $\Sigma c_n z^n$ which has been found.

18. Convergence of the power series.

THEOREM 16. *With the notation of* § 17, *suppose that* $zp(z)$ *and* $z^2q(z)$ *are regular for* $|z| < R$. *Then the series obtained corresponding to a value* ρ *satisfying the indicial equation converges for* $|z| < R$.

PROOF. If the series terminates, this is true; suppose that it is an infinite series. Let ρ' be the other root of the indicial equation.

From (17.1), c_n is given by

$$n(n+\rho - \rho')c_n = -\sum_{s=0}^{n-1} c_s\{(\rho + s)p_{n-s} + q_{n-s}\}. \quad (18.1)$$

We enter upon a *majorising* argument, replacing every c_n by a number C_n such that $|c_n| \leqq C_n$.

Let r be any number less than R. By Cauchy's inequality there is a number $K = K(r)$,[†] independent of n, for which

$$|p_n| \leqq \frac{K}{r^n}, \quad |q_n| \leqq \frac{K}{r^n} \quad (n = 0, 1, 2, \ldots).$$

The modulus of the right-hand side of (18.1) is then less than or equal to

$$K\sum_{s=0}^{n-1}|c_s|\frac{|\rho| + s + 1}{r^{n-s}}.$$

† Phillips, *Functions of a Complex Variable*, p. 96, Corollary.

Write $|\rho - \rho'| = \lambda$, $|\rho| = \mu$, and define C_n by the rules

$$C_n = |c_n| \text{ for } 0 \leqq n < \lambda,$$

$$C_n n(n - \lambda) = K \sum_{s=0}^{n-1} C_s \frac{\mu + s + 1}{r^{n-s}} \text{ for } n \geqq \lambda. \quad (18.2)$$

From (18.2) we shall show that, as $n \to \infty$,

$$\frac{C_n}{C_{n-1}} \to \frac{1}{r}. \quad (18.3)$$

For subtract the $(n - 1)^{\text{th}}$ equation of the type (18.2) divided through by r from the nth and we have

$$n(n - \lambda)C_n - (n - 1)(n - 1 - \lambda)\frac{C_{n-1}}{r} = K(\mu + n)\frac{C_{n-1}}{r}.$$

Divide through by $C_{n-1}n(n - \lambda)$, let $n \to \infty$ and we obtain (18.3).

Therefore the radius of convergence of $\Sigma\, C_n z^n$ is r. But, from the definition of the C_n, we have $|c_n| \leqq C_n$. Therefore the radius of convergence of $\Sigma c_n z^n$ is at least r. But r is any number less than R. Therefore $\Sigma c_n z^n$ converges for $|z| < R$, and this is what we set out to prove.

19. The second solution when exponents are equal or differ by an integer.

Let $w = w_0(z) = z^\rho(c_0 + c_1 z + \ldots + c_n z^n + \ldots)$ be the one solution obtained. Let ρ' be the other root of the indicial equation; we shall write ν for the positive integer $\rho - \rho' + 1$. From the indicial equation $\rho + \rho' = 1 - p_0$, and so $2\rho + p_0 = \nu$.

The method of reduction of order (§ 9) will be used to find a second solution from the known solution w_0. Write $w = w_0 v$, and the equation for v is

$$w_0 v'' + \{2w_0' + p(z)w_0\}v' = 0,$$

from which

$$v' = \frac{A}{w_0^2} \exp\left\{-\int^z p(\zeta)d\zeta\right\}$$

$$= \frac{A}{z^{2\rho}(c_0 + c_1 z + \ldots)^2} \exp(-p_0 \log z - p_1 z - \tfrac{1}{2}p_2 z^2 - \ldots)$$

$$= \frac{A}{z^{\nu}(c_0 + c_1 z + \ldots)^2} \exp(- p_1 z - \tfrac{1}{2}p_2 z^2 - \ldots)$$

$$= \frac{A}{z^{\nu}} \, g(z),$$

where $g(z)$ is regular at the origin and $g(0) = 1/c_0^2$. In a circle, centre $z = 0$, $g(z)$ can be expanded in a Taylor series

$$a_0 + a_1 z + \ldots, \, (a_0 \neq 0).$$

Integrate v' to obtain v, and we have for the second solution any constant multiple of

$$w_0(z) \left\{ - \frac{a_0}{(\nu - 1)z^{\nu-1}} - \ldots - \frac{a_{\nu-2}}{z} + a_{\nu-1} \log z + a_\nu z + \ldots \right\}.$$

This is

$$a_{\nu-1}w_0(z) \log z + z^{\rho'} \sum_{n=0}^{\infty} b_n z^n. \tag{19.1}$$

If the roots of the indicial equation are equal, $\nu = 1$ and $\rho' = \rho$, and since $a_0 \neq 0$, the term in $\log z$ is always present.

For roots differing by an integer, it may happen that $a_{\nu-1} = 0$, and in that case there is no logarithmic term.

20. The method of Frobenius. It will be noticed that in § 19 there is no means of finding the general term in the expansion of $g(z)$, and so we look for other methods better adapted to giving the general term in the solution. One way would be to substitute the known form (19.1) of the solution in the equation and find the b_n by equating coefficients of powers of z. Another method is that of Frobenius (1873), which will now be explained.

Assume as before

$$w = z^{\rho}(c_0 + c_1 z + \ldots).$$

Let ρ_1 and ρ_2 be the exponents. The equation (17.1) for c_n is

$$c_n(\rho + n - \rho_1)(\rho + n - \rho_2) + \sum_{s=0}^{n-1} c_s\{(\rho + s)p_{n-s} + q_{n-s}\} = 0.$$

Insert in the series the values of the coefficients c_n in terms of ρ, but do not yet put ρ equal to ρ_1 or ρ_2, and we have an expansion

$$w = c_0 W = c_0 z^\rho \{1 + z f_1(\rho) + \ldots + z^n f_n(\rho) + \ldots\},$$

where

$$\left\{\frac{d^2}{dz^2} + p(z)\frac{d}{dz} + q(z)\right\} W = z^{\rho-2}(\rho - \rho_1)(\rho - \rho_2).$$

Differentiate each side with respect to ρ. The order of differentiation with respect to z and ρ may be interchanged, and so

$$\left\{\frac{d^2}{dz^2} + p(z)\frac{d}{dz} + q(z)\right\} \frac{dW}{d\rho} = \frac{d}{d\rho}\{z^{\rho-2}(\rho - \rho_1)(\rho - \rho_2)\}.$$

(i) EQUAL ROOTS. $\rho_1 = \rho_2$.
The right-hand side is 0 for $\rho = \rho_1$, and so

$$(W)_{\rho_1} \text{ and } \left(\frac{dW}{d\rho}\right)_{\rho_1} \text{ are solutions.}$$

$$\left(\frac{dW}{d\rho}\right)_{\rho_1} = z^{\rho_1} \log z\{1 + z f_1(\rho_1) + \ldots\} + z^{\rho_1}\{z f_1'(\rho_1) + \ldots\},$$

which is of the form found in § 19.

Note that the $f_n(\rho)$ are rational functions, and so $f_n'(\rho_1)$ is best calculated by logarithmic differentiation.

(ii) ROOTS DIFFERING BY AN INTEGER. $\rho_1 = \rho_2 + n$.
$(W)_{\rho_1}$ is a solution. In general the f's from $f_n(\rho)$ onwards have a factor $\rho - \rho_2$ in the denominator. Write

$$W_1 = (\rho - \rho_2)W.$$

Then

$$\left\{\frac{d^2}{dz^2} + p(z)\frac{d}{dz} + q(z)\right\} W_1 = z^{\rho-2}(\rho - \rho_1)(\rho - \rho_2)^2.$$

Possible solutions are $(W_1)_{\rho_1}$, $(W_1)_{\rho_2}$, $\left(\frac{dW_1}{d\rho}\right)_{\rho_2}$. The second of these is a multiple of the first (the lowest power of z in each is z^{ρ_1}), and the third is the solution we are seeking.

For an example in which there is a factor $\rho - \rho_2$ in the numerator of $f_n(\rho)$ cancelling the one in the denominator, so that the solution with exponent ρ_2 is valid, see §22 (iii).

21. The point at infinity. In complex variable theory, the plane in which values of the variable z are represented is completed by the addition of a single point at infinity.[†]

The point $z = \infty$ is an ordinary point of the equation

$$w'' + p(z)w' + q(z)w = 0$$

if $2z - z^2 p(z)$ *and* $z^4 q(z)$

are regular at $z = \infty$.

It is a regular singularity if $zp(z)$ and $z^2q(z)$ are regular.

Put $z = 1/\zeta$, so that $z = \infty$ corresponds to $\zeta = 0$, and denote differentiations with respect to ζ by dots. Then

$$w' = -\dot{w}\zeta^2,$$
$$w'' = \ddot{w}\zeta^4 + 2\dot{w}\zeta^3.$$

So the equation with ζ as independent variable is

$$\ddot{w} + \left\{ \frac{2}{\zeta} - \frac{1}{\zeta^2} p\left(\frac{1}{\zeta}\right) \right\} \dot{w} + \frac{1}{\zeta^4} q\left(\frac{1}{\zeta}\right) w = 0.$$

The conditions for $\zeta = 0$ to be an ordinary point are that the coefficients of $\dot{w}$ and w shall be regular at $\zeta = 0$. This gives the first result.

Also $\zeta = 0$ is a regular singularity if

$$\frac{1}{\zeta} p\left(\frac{1}{\zeta}\right) \text{ and } \frac{1}{\zeta^2} q\left(\frac{1}{\zeta}\right)$$

are regular at $\zeta = 0$. This gives the second result.

22. Bessel's equation. An illustration of the method of § 20 is provided by Bessel's equation

$$z^2 w'' + zw' + (z^2 - \nu^2)w = 0$$

† Phillips, *Functions of a Complex Variable*, p. 9 and p. 102.

(where ν is a constant), which will be investigated more fully in Chapter VIII. The point $z = 0$ is a regular singularity, and we shall obtain solutions in the cases (i) $\nu = 0$, (ii) $\nu = 1$, (iii) $\nu = \frac{1}{2}$.

Put

$$w = z^\rho(c_0 + c_1 z + \ldots + c_n z^n + \ldots)$$

in the equation, and equate coefficients of powers of z. We have

$$c_0(\rho^2 - \nu^2) = 0,$$
$$c_1\{(\rho + 1)^2 - \nu^2\} = 0,$$
$$c_n\{(\rho + n)^2 - \nu^2\} + c_{n-2} = 0, \quad (n \geqq 2).$$

The indicial equation gives $\rho = \nu$ or $\rho = -\nu$.

(i) $\nu = 0$. Here the exponents are equal. We write

$$W = z^\rho \left\{ 1 - \frac{z^2}{(\rho+2)^2} + \ldots + \frac{(-1)^n z^{2n}}{(\rho+2)^2 \ldots (\rho+2n)^2} + \ldots \right\}.$$

Then $w_1 = (W)_{\rho=0}$ and $w_2 = \left(\dfrac{\partial W}{\partial \rho}\right)_{\rho=0}$ are solutions. We have

$$w_1 = 1 - \frac{z^2}{2^2} + \ldots + (-1)^n \frac{z^{2n}}{2^{2n}(n!)^2} + \ldots,$$

$$w_2 = w_1 \log z + \sum_{n=1}^\infty \frac{(-1)^{n-1} z^{2n}}{2^{2n}(n!)^2} \left(1 + \frac{1}{2} + \ldots + \frac{1}{n}\right).$$

The general solution is $w = A w_1 + B w_2$.

(ii) $\nu = 1$. The exponents are $\rho = 1$ and $\rho = -1$, differing by an integer. In the notation of § 20 (ii),

$$W_1 = z^\rho \left\{ (\rho + 1) - \frac{z^2}{\rho + 3} + \frac{z^4}{(\rho+3)^2(\rho+5)} - \ldots \right\}.$$

$\rho = 1$ gives the solution

$$w_1 = z \left\{ 2 - \frac{z^2}{4} + \frac{z^4}{4^2 \cdot 6} - \frac{z^6}{4^2 \cdot 6^2 \cdot 8} + \ldots \right\}.$$

A second solution is $(\partial W_1/\partial\rho)_{\rho=-1}$ or

$$w_2 = \log z \left\{ -\frac{z}{2} + \frac{z^3}{2^2.4} - \frac{z^5}{2^2.4^2.6} + \ldots \right\} +$$

$$z^{-1}\left\{1 + \frac{z^2}{2^2} - \frac{z^4}{2^2.4}\left(\frac{2}{2}+\frac{1}{4}\right) + \frac{z^6}{2^2.4^2.6}\left(\frac{2}{2}+\frac{2}{4}+\frac{1}{6}\right) + \ldots\right\},$$

the coefficient of $\log z$ being $-\frac{1}{4}w_1$.

(iii) $\nu = \frac{1}{2}$. The exponents $\frac{1}{2}$, $-\frac{1}{2}$ again differ by an integer, but here the solution contains no term in $\log z$. $\rho = \frac{1}{2}$ gives

$$w = c_0 z^{\frac{1}{2}} \left(1 - \frac{z^2}{3!} + \frac{z^4}{5!} - \ldots\right)$$

$\rho = -\frac{1}{2}$ gives

$$w = c_0 z^{-\frac{1}{2}}\left(1 - \frac{z^2}{2!} + \frac{z^4}{4!} - \ldots\right) + c_1 z^{-\frac{1}{2}}\left(z - \frac{z^3}{3!} + \frac{z^5}{5!} - \ldots\right).$$

This is the complete solution, the coefficient of c_1 being a repetition of the solution obtained from $\rho = \frac{1}{2}$.

It happens that the solution can be expressed in finite form

$$z^{-\frac{1}{2}}(c_0 \cos z + c_1 \sin z).$$

Examples.

By the trial solution $w = z^\rho(c_0 + c_1 z + \ldots)$ or otherwise, solve completely the equations 1—12

1. $4z(1-z)w'' + 2(1-2z)w' + w = 0$.

2. $(2z + 4z^3)w'' - w' - 24zw = 0$.

3. $z^2w'' + zw' + (z^2 - k^2)w = 0$ for $k = \frac{1}{3}$ and for $k = 2$.

4. $z(1-z)w'' - (1+z)w' + w = 0$.

5. $z^2(1+z)w'' - z(1+2z)w' + (1+2z)w = 0$.

6. $zw'' + w' - 4zw = 0$.

7. $w''' = zw$.

8. $zw'' = w$.

9. $z^2(1-z)^2w'' + z(1-z)(1-2z)w' - w = 0$.

10. $2(2 - z)z^2w'' - (4 - z)zw' + (3 - z)w = 0.$

11. $zw'' + (1 + 4z^2)w' + 4z(1 + z^2)w = 0.$

12. $z^2w'' - (5z + kz^2)w' + (5 + 3kz)w = 0.$

13. Integrate the equation

$$xy'' + ky' - y = 0$$

by the method of solution in series (i) when the constant k is not an integer, (ii) when $k = 1$.

Express the general solution in finite form when $k = \frac{1}{2}$.

14. Find a solution as a power series in x of the equation

$$x(x - 1)y'' + 3xy' + y = 0,$$

and state where the series converges. Identify the rational function of x represented by the series and derive a second independent solution of the differential equation.

15. Integrate in series the equation

$$x(1 - 4x)y'' + \{(4p - 6)x - p + 1\}y' - p(p - 1)y = 0,$$

and express the solution in the form

$$A\{1 + (1 - 4x)^{\frac{1}{2}}\}^p + B\{1 - (1 - 4x)^{\frac{1}{2}}\}^p.$$

16. Find the complete solution in series to the equation

$$x(1 + 2x^2)y'' + 2y' - 12xy = 0,$$

and give the range of values of x for which it is valid.

17. Solve in series the equation

$$zw'' + (p + q + z)w' + pw = 0,$$

with particular reference to the case $p + q = 1$.

18. Solve in series the equation

$$zw'' + (2 + az)w' + (a + bz)w = 0.$$

(The recurrence relation connecting the coefficients contains three terms c_n, c_{n-1}, c_{n-2}. Such a relation determines c_n as an explicit function of n only if, as in this example, it is of a special form. For an illustration of a method of dealing with three-term relations which cannot be explicitly solved, see Jeffreys and Jeffreys, *Methods of Mathematical Physics*, p. 485).

19. Solve the equation

$$z^2(1 + z)^2 w'' + z(1 - z^2)w' + (1 + z + 2z^2)w = 0$$

(The indicial equation has complex roots. In all preceding examples
the roots have been real, and this is the important case in practice.
For a complex exponent the solution will contain cosines and sines
of multiples of $\log z$, and the behaviour of these functions near $z = 0$
does not correspond to natural phenomena).

20. Show that the differential equation

$$y' = y^2 + x^2, \quad y(0) = 0,$$

can be formally solved by a power series

$$y = \tfrac{1}{3}x^3(1 + \sum_{n=1}^{\infty} a_n x^{4n});$$

find a recurrence relation for the coefficient a_n, and deduce that the
series converges for $x^4 < 12$.

Compare your solution with the solution of the differential equation

$$z' = z^2 + 1, \quad z(1) = y(1)$$

and deduce that the series diverges for $x = 1 + \tfrac{1}{2}\pi$.

CHAPTER V

SINGULARITIES OF EQUATIONS

23. Solutions near a singularity. In Chapter IV solutions in the form of infinite series were obtained near a *regular singularity* of a differential equation. The following discussion throws further light on the distinction between regular and irregular singularities.

In the equation

$$w'' + p(z)w' + q(z)w = 0,$$

we suppose that $z = 0$ is a singularity of one or both of $p(z)$ and $q(z)$ and that there is a circle S with centre $z = 0$ in which they are one-valued and have no other singularities. If z_0 is any point (not 0) inside S, there are two linearly independent solutions of the equation

$$w'' + p(z)w' + q(z)w = 0,$$

say $w_1(z)$ and $w_2(z)$, regular in a circle centre z_0. These solutions have analytic continuations along a path in S enclosing the origin and returning to z_0. Let the functions so obtained as the continuations of $w_1(z)$ and $w_2(z)$ be $W_1(z)$ and $W_2(z)$ respectively.

The functions obtained at each step of the process of continuation satisfy the differential equation, and any solution is the sum of constant multiples of the functions of a fundamental set. Therefore

$$W_1(z) = aw_1(z) + bw_2(z)$$
$$W_2(z) = cw_1(z) + dw_2(z)$$

where $ad - bc \neq 0$. (If $ad = bc$, then $cW_1(z) - aW_2(z) \equiv 0$, and so, carrying out the analytic continuation in the opposite direction along the path, $cw_1(z) - aw_2(z) \equiv 0$ which contradicts the linear independence of w_1 and w_2.)

We now find the condition that a solution when continued round $z = 0$ is unaltered except for a constant multiplier.

Any solution w, regular at z_0, can be expressed as

$$\alpha w_1 + \beta w_2.$$

By continuation round $z = 0$ this becomes

$$\alpha(aw_1 + bw_2) + \beta(cw_1 + dw_2).$$

This expression is of the form $\lambda(\alpha w_1 + \beta w_2)$ if

$$\alpha(a - \lambda) + \beta c = 0,$$

and

$$\alpha b + \beta(d - \lambda) = 0;$$

i.e. λ must satisfy $\begin{vmatrix} a - \lambda & c \\ b & d - \lambda \end{vmatrix} = 0.$ (23.1)

CASE (i) UNEQUAL ROOTS λ_1, λ_2.

We can take a new fundamental set of solutions at z_0, calling $w_1(z)$ the solution which acquires the multiplier λ_1, and $w_2(z)$ that which acquires the multiplier λ_2.

The function z^ρ acquires a multiplier $e^{2\pi i \rho}$ in going round $z = 0$. So, if $2\pi i \rho_1 = \log \lambda_1$ and $2\pi i \rho_2 = \log \lambda_2$, then $z^{-\rho_1} w_1(z)$ and $z^{-\rho_2} w_2(z)$ are single-valued in S and can be expanded in Laurent series. So we have the *canonical* fundamental set of solutions near the singularity $z = 0$

$$w_1(z) = z^{\rho_1} \sum_{-\infty}^{\infty} a_n z^n, \quad w_2(z) = z^{\rho_2} \sum_{-\infty}^{\infty} b_n z^n. \quad (23.2)$$

CASE (ii) EQUAL ROOTS λ_1.

There is, as in case (i), a solution w_1 whose continuation is $W_1 = \lambda_1 w_1$. Suppose that W_2 is the continuation of $cw_1 + dw_2$. Then the equation corresponding to (23.1)

$$\begin{vmatrix} \lambda_1 - \lambda & c \\ 0 & d - \lambda \end{vmatrix} = 0$$

has equal roots $\lambda = \lambda_1$. So $d = \lambda_1$ and

$$\frac{W_2}{W_1} = \frac{w_2}{w_1} + \frac{c}{\lambda_1},$$

that is to say, w_2/w_1 is increased by c/λ_1 when z goes round the origin. Therefore

$$\frac{w_2}{w_1} - \frac{c}{2\pi i \lambda_1} \log z$$

is single-valued in S and can be expanded in a Laurent series. This gives for the canonical fundamental set in the equal-root case

$$w_1(z) = z^{\rho_1} \sum_{-\infty}^{\infty} a_n z^n,$$

$$w_2(z) = z^{\rho_1} \sum_{-\infty}^{\infty} b_n z^n + k w_1(z) \log z. \qquad (23.3)$$

24. Regular and irregular singularities. The process set out in § 23 of investigating solutions which acquire a constant multiplier by analytic continuation round a singularity is not a practical one for the calculation of coefficients in the solutions, and we must think of ways of finding the a_n and b_n in the canonical forms. The most natural is to assume $w = z^{\rho} \sum_{-\infty}^{\infty} a_n z^n$, substitute in the differential equation and equate coefficients of powers of z. If we do this (on the lines of § 17) it is apparent that the Laurent series will give rise to equations containing infinitely many unknowns, and they are manageable only if the Laurent series contain finitely many negative powers. It is this case which is singled out as a **regular singularity**. The best definition is now seen to be the following.

DEFINITION. An isolated singularity $z = a$ of a differential equation is called **regular** if there is a constant k such that, for every solution $w(z)$,

$$(z - a)^k w(z) \to 0 \text{ as } z \to a.$$

The singularity is called **irregular** if it is not regular.

It is clear that, if the Laurent series have only finitely many negative powers, the singularity is regular according to the definition. The converse is true. For, choosing k to be $m - \rho_1$ where m is a integer, we have for w_1, $\sum_{-\infty}^{\infty} a_n(z - a)^n \to 0$ as $z \to a$, from which $a_n = 0$ for $n \leqq 0$. A similar remark holds for w_2.

The next theorem shows that the definition of regular singularity just given accords with the usage of Chapter IV. We again take $a = 0$ for brevity.

THEOREM 17. *Necessary and sufficient conditions for $z = 0$ to be a regular singularity of the equation*

$$w'' + p(z)w' + q(z)w = 0$$

are that $zp(z)$ and $z^2q(z)$ are regular at $z = 0$ (at least one of $p(z)$ and $q(z)$ having a singularity there).

PROOF. The sufficiency has already been established by the finding of the solutions in §§ 17 − 19. We prove the necessity.

From (23.2) and (23.3) we have solutions

$$w_1(z) = z^{\rho_1} \Sigma a_n z^n,$$
$$w_2(z) = z^{\rho_2} \Sigma b_n z^n + k w_1(z) \log z,$$

where $\rho_2 = \rho_1$ if $k \neq 0$, and in which the Laurent series have finitely many negative powers.

Since w_1 and w_2 satisfy the differential equation, we have

$$p(z) = -\frac{w_1 w_2'' - w_1'' w_2}{w_1 w_2' - w_1' w_2} = -\frac{d}{dz}\left[\log\left\{w_1^2 \frac{d}{dz}\left(\frac{w_2}{w_1}\right)\right\}\right]$$

$$= -\frac{2w_1'}{w_1} - \frac{\dfrac{d^2}{dz^2}\left(\dfrac{w_2}{w_1}\right)}{\dfrac{d}{dz}\left(\dfrac{w_2}{w_1}\right)}.$$

Now $\dfrac{w_2}{w_1} = k \log z + z^{\rho_2 - \rho_1 + m} \sum\limits_0^\infty c_n z^n$, where m is an integer, $c_0 \neq 0$, and $\rho_2 = \rho_1$ if $k \neq 0$. Consequently,

$$\frac{d}{dz}\left(\frac{w_2}{w_1}\right) = \frac{k}{z} + z^{\rho_2 - \rho_1 + m - 1} \sum_0^\infty d_n z^n,$$

$$\frac{d^2}{dz^2}\left(\frac{w_2}{w_1}\right) = -\frac{k}{z^2} + z^{\rho_2 - \rho_1 + m - 2} \sum_0^\infty e_n z^n.$$

The quotient of the last expression by the preceding is regular or has a pole of order one at $z = 0$; the same is true of w_1'/w_1, and therefore of $p(z)$.

Since w_1 satisfies the given differential equation, we have

$$q(z) = -\frac{w_1''}{w_1} - p(z)\frac{w_1'}{w_1}.$$

Since w_1'/w_1, w_1''/w_1' and $p(z)$ are regular or have poles of order one, therefore $q(z)$ is regular or has a pole of order one or two. This proves the theorem.

25. Equations with assigned singularities. In this section we admit only second-order differential equations whose singularities for finite z or for $z = \infty$ are regular. [†]

There is at least one finite value of z for which such an equation has a singularity, unless the equation is $w'' = 0$.

For an equation with no singularity for a finite z is of the form

$$w'' + p(z)w' + q(z)w = 0,$$

where $p(z)$ and $q(z)$ are regular for all finite z. But unless $p(z) = q(z) = 0$, the singularity for $z = \infty$ is irregular.

An equation whose only finite singularity is at $z = a$ is of the form

$$w'' + \frac{b}{z-a}w' + \frac{c}{(z-a)^2}w = 0, \quad (b, c \text{ constants}).$$

This equation has a singularity at $z = \infty$ unless $b = 2$, $c = 0$.

† See §§ 16, 17, 21.

For the general equation with a singularity at a is

$$w'' + \frac{p(z)}{z - a} w' + \frac{q(z)}{(z - a)^2} w = 0,$$

where $p(z)$ and $q(z)$ are regular for all finite z.

From § 21, the singularity at $z = \infty$ can only be regular if $p(z)$ and $q(z)$ are constants. From § 21 again, the conditions for $z = \infty$ to be an ordinary point are $b = 2$, $c = 0$, in which case the equation integrates to

$$w = \frac{A}{z - a} + B.$$

Equation with two singularities. If the singularities are at $z = a$, $z = b$, while $z = \infty$ is an ordinary point, we can reduce this case to the last by the transformation $\zeta = (z - a)/(z - b)$, which gives an equation in ζ with 0 and ∞ as singularities.

26. The hypergeometric equation. We next consider equations with three regular singularities. Any three points can be transformed by a bilinear substitution into 0, 1, ∞. † We shall obtain a standard form of equation having singularities at 0, 1, ∞.

Take the equation

$$w'' + p(z)w' + q(z)w = 0.$$

Then $z(1 - z)p(z)$ and $z^2(1 - z)^2 q(z)$ are regular for all finite z and $zp(z)$, $z^2 q(z)$ are regular for $z = \infty$. So the most general forms of $p(z)$ and $q(z)$ are

$$p(z) = \frac{p_0 + p_1 z}{z(1 - z)}, \quad q(z) = \frac{q_0 + q_1 z + q_2 z^2}{z^2(1 - z)^2},$$

We may, by a change of dependent variable

$$w = z^\alpha (1 - z)^\beta W,$$

suppose that for each of the values $z = 0$ and $z = 1$ one of the two exponents is zero.

† Phillips, *Functions of a Complex Variable*, p. 40.

If, then,

$$w = c_0 + c_1 z + \ldots, \quad (c_0 \neq 0)$$

satisfies the equation, we find by substituting in the equation that $q_0 = 0$, so that z is a factor of the numerator of $q(z)$. So, for the same reason, is $1 - z$. The equation is now reduced to

$$z(1 - z)w'' + (p_0 + p_1 z)w' + q_1 w = 0.$$

The coefficients p_0, p_1, q_1 are most conveniently expressed in terms of the exponents at $z = \infty$, and the exponent other than zero at $z = 0$. Let the exponents at ∞ be a, b.

Putting

$$w = \frac{1}{z^\rho} \left(c_0 + \frac{c_1}{z} + \ldots \right)$$

we find the indicial equation at ∞ to be

$$- \rho(\rho + 1) - p_1 \rho + q_1 = 0.$$

If the roots are a, b, then

$$ab = - q_1, \quad a + b = - p_1 - 1.$$

The final form of the equation is

$$z(1 - z)w'' + \{c - (a + b + 1)z\}w' - abw = 0, \quad (26.1)$$

where the remaining exponent at $z = 0$ is $1 - c$.

This is the **hypergeometric equation.**

27. The hypergeometric function. Solutions of (26.1) near $z = 0$ are given by

$$w = z^\rho(c_0 + c_1 z + \ldots + c_n z^n + \ldots).$$

We know already that $\rho = 0$ or $1 - c$. The recurrence relation is found to be

$$c_{n+1} = \frac{(\rho + n + a)(\rho + n + b)}{(\rho + n + 1)(\rho + n + c)} c_n.$$

If c is not a negative integer, $\rho = 0$ gives the solution

$$1 + \frac{a \cdot b}{1 \cdot c} z + \ldots$$

$$+ \frac{a(a+1)\ldots(a+n-1)b(b+1)\ldots(b+n-1)}{n!c(c+1)\ldots(c+n-1)} z^n + \ldots$$

This series will be called $F(a, b; c; z)$, the **hypergeometric function.** The radius of convergence of the series is found to be 1; this could also be predicted from the fact that the singularity nearest to $z = 0$ is $z = 1$.

The second solution near $z = 0$ is

$$z^{1-c}F(a - c + 1, b - c + 1; 2 - c; z),$$

on the assumption that c is not an integer. In further work with hypergeometric functions, we shall assume that the exponents at any singularity under consideration do not differ by zero or an integer.

With three parameters a, b, c at our disposal, it is easy to fit many common functions into hypergeometric form, for example

$$(1 - z)^n = F(-n, 1; 1; z),$$
$$\log(1 - z) = -zF(1, 1; 2; z),$$
$$\text{arc sin } z = zF(\tfrac{1}{2}, \tfrac{1}{2}; \tfrac{3}{2}; z^2).$$

28. Expression of $F(a, b; c; z)$ as an integral. We assume throughout this section that $\mathbf{R}c > \mathbf{R}b > 0$.

THEOREM 18.

$$F(a, b; c; z) = \frac{\Gamma(c)}{\Gamma(b)\Gamma(c-b)} \int_0^1 t^{b-1}(1 - t)^{c-b-1}(1 - zt)^{-a} dt, \tag{28.1}$$

where $(1 - zt)^{-a}$ *has its principal value.*

PROOF. If $|z| < 1$,

$$\frac{\Gamma(a)\Gamma(b)}{\Gamma(c)} F(a, b; c; z) = \sum_{n=0}^{\infty} \frac{\Gamma(a+n)\Gamma(b+n)}{\Gamma(1+n)\Gamma(c+n)} z^n, \tag{28.2}$$

From the first Eulerian integral [†]

$$\frac{\Gamma(b+n)\Gamma(c-b)}{\Gamma(c+n)} = B(b+n, c-b) = \int_0^1 t^{b+n-1}(1-t)^{c-b-1} dt.$$

The right-hand side of (28.2) may therefore be written

$$\frac{1}{\Gamma(c-b)} \sum_{n=0}^\infty \int_0^1 t^{b+n-1}(1-t)^{c-b-1} \Gamma(a+n) \frac{z^n}{n!} dt.$$

If $|z| < 1$, the series $\sum \Gamma(a+n) \frac{z^n t^n}{n!}$ converges uniformly with respect to t for $0 \le t \le 1$. So

$$\sum_{n=0}^\infty \int_0^1 dt = \int_0^1 dt \sum_{n=0}^\infty,$$

and the right-hand side of (28.2) becomes

$$\frac{1}{\Gamma(c-b)} \int_0^1 t^{b-1}(1-t)^{c-b-1} \sum_{n=0}^\infty \Gamma(a+n) \frac{z^n t^n}{n!} dt$$
$$= \frac{\Gamma(a)}{\Gamma(c-b)} \int_0^1 t^{b-1}(1-t)^{c-b-1}(1-zt)^{-a} dt.$$

This gives (28.1). The right-hand side of (28.1) is a regular function of z in the whole plane, cut along the real axis from 1 to $+\infty$. This provides the analytic continuation of $F(a, b; c; z)$ outside the circle $|z| < 1$ in which it was defined by the series.

29. Formulae connecting hypergeometric functions. There are vast numbers of relations connecting hypergeometric functions with different parameters, and we give only a few, choosing those which rest on interesting work in convergence or manipulation of gamma-functions. We prove first

THEOREM 19. *If* $\mathbf{R}(c-a-b) > 0$, *the series for* $F(a, b; c; 1)$ *converges and*

$$F(a, b; c; 1) = \frac{\Gamma(c)\Gamma(c-a-b)}{\Gamma(c-a)\Gamma(c-b)}.$$

[†] Gillespie, *Integration*, § 38.

PROOF. If u_n is the nth term in the series for $F(a, b; c; 1)$,

$$\frac{u_n}{u_{n+1}} = \frac{(1+n)(c+n)}{(a+n)(b+n)} = 1 + \frac{c-a-b+1}{n} + O\left(\frac{1}{n^2}\right).$$

Convergence is shown by Gauss's test.

Then, from Abel's limit theorem, [†]

$$F(a, b; c; 1) = \lim_{x \to 1-0} F(a, b; c; x)$$

$$= \lim_{x \to 1-0} \frac{\Gamma(c)}{\Gamma(b)\Gamma(c-b)} \int_0^1 t^{b-1}(1-t)^{c-b-1}(1-xt)^{-a}\,dt, \text{ from (28.1)}$$

$$= \frac{\Gamma(c)}{\Gamma(b)\Gamma(c-b)} \int_0^1 t^{b-1}(1-t)^{c-a-b-1}\,dt,$$

since this last integral exists, and $(1-xt)^{-a} \to (1-t)^{-a}$ uniformly for $0 \leq t \leq 1$ if $\mathbf{R}a \leq 0$, whereas, if $\mathbf{R}a > 0$,

$$|(1-xt)^{-a}| \leq |(1-t)^{-a}|$$

in which case Weierstrass's M-test for integrals applies. Since

$$\int_0^1 t^{b-1}(1-t)^{c-a-b-1}\,dt = \frac{\Gamma(b)\Gamma(c-a-b)}{\Gamma(c-a)},$$

we have the result.

This method of proof is subject to the limitation of § 28 that $\mathbf{R}c > \mathbf{R}b > 0$. The result, however, is true independently of this.

Finally we prove a formula connecting hypergeometric functions of z and $1-z$.

The solutions convergent for $|z| < 1$ are

$$F(a, b; c; z), \tag{i}$$

$$z^{1-c}F(a-c+1, b-c+1; 2-c; z). \tag{ii}$$

If we write $z = 1 - \zeta$ in the hypergeometric equation (26.1), it becomes

$$\zeta(1-\zeta)\frac{d^2w}{d\zeta^2} + \{(a+b-c+1) - (a+b+1)\zeta\}\frac{dw}{d\zeta} - abw = 0.$$

† For the O-notation, Gauss's test and Abel's theorem, see Hyslop, *Infinite Series*, pp. 14, 49, 80.

Writing down the solutions of this equation valid for $|\zeta| < 1$ and replacing ζ by $1 - z$, we have

$$F(a, b; a + b - c + 1; 1 - z), \qquad \text{(iii)}$$
$$(1 - z)^{c-a-b}F(c - b, c - a; c - a - b + 1; 1 - z). \qquad \text{(iv)}$$

The functions (i)—(iv) are solutions of the hypergeometric equation in the domain common to the circles $|z| < 1$, $|1 - z| < 1$. There must be two linear identities connecting them. One of these is

$$\text{(i)} = A\text{(iii)} + B\text{(iv)}.$$

We shall obtain the constants A, B. Let $z \to 1$ along the real axis. We have

$$\frac{\Gamma(c)\Gamma(c - a - b)}{\Gamma(c - a)\Gamma(c - b)} = A.$$

Similarly $z \to 0$ gives

$$1 = A\frac{\Gamma(a+b-c+1)\Gamma(1-c)}{\Gamma(a-c+1)\Gamma(b-c+1)} + B\frac{\Gamma(c-a-b+1)\Gamma(1-c)}{\Gamma(1-b)\Gamma(1-a)}.$$

After some manipulation we can deduce that

$$B = \frac{\Gamma(c)\Gamma(a+b-c)}{\Gamma(a)\Gamma(b)}.$$

30. Confluence of singularities.

The function e^z is not of the form $F(a, b; c; z)$. It can, however, easily be shown to be $\lim\limits_{b \to \infty} F(a, b; a; z/b)$.

The equation of which $F(a, b; c; z/b)$ is a solution is

$$z\left(1 - \frac{z}{b}\right)w'' + \left(c - z - \frac{a + 1}{b}z\right)w' - aw = 0.$$

This has regular singularities at $0, b, \infty$. When $b \to \infty$, we have the *confluence* of the two singularities b, ∞. The equation then becomes

$$zw'' + (c - z)w' - aw = 0,$$

with a regular singularity at $z = 0$ and a singularity at ∞ that is easily seen to be irregular.

Information about solutions of this last equation is more easily obtained directly than by limiting operations on hypergeometric functions.

Examples.

1. Prove that the solutions of

$$zw'' - (1 + z)w' + w = 0$$

in powers of z are regular at $z = 0$.

A value such as $z = 0$ in this equation which, according to the definition, is a singularity of the equation but at which the solutions are regular may be called an apparent singularity.

2. For the equation

$$z^2w'' + (1 + z)w' - aw = 0,$$

which has an irregular singularity at $z = 0$, prove that, in general there is no solution of the form $z^k r(z)$, where $r(z)$ is regular at $z = 0$; if, however, a is the square of an integer there is one such solution. Obtain this solution when $a = 4$.

3. Prove that the equation

$$z^3w'' + z^2w' + w = 0$$

has no solution $z^k r(z)$, where $r(z)$ is regular at $z = 0$.

Prove that $z = \infty$ is a regular singularity of the equation.

4. Prove that there is a solution of the equation

$$z^3(1 + z)w'' + z(1 + 2z)w' - (1 + 2z)w = 0$$

regular at $z = 0$.

Find also a solution regular at $z = \infty$, and write down the general solution of the equation.

5. Prove that, if $|z| < 1$,

$$\int_0^{\pi/2} \frac{d\theta}{\sqrt{\{1 - z \sin^2 \theta\}}} = \tfrac{1}{2}\pi F(\tfrac{1}{2}, \tfrac{1}{2}; 1; z).$$

6. Prove that, if $a - b$ is not an integer, the general solution of the hypergeometric equation in powers of $1/z$ is

$$Az^{-a}F(a, a-c+1; a-b+1; 1/z) + Bz^{-b}F(b, b-c+1; b-a+1; 1/z).$$

7. Prove that

$$F(a, b; c; z) = (1 - z)^{-a}F\left(a, c - b; c; \frac{z}{z - 1}\right).$$

CHAPTER VI

CONTOUR INTEGRAL SOLUTIONS

31. Solutions expressed as integrals. Because solutions of a differential equation cannot in general be expressed as a finite combination of elementary functions, we were led in Chapter IV to investigate solutions expressed as infinite series of such functions (powers of $z - a$). Another common way of carrying out a limiting process on elementary functions is by integration with respect to a parameter e.g.

$$\varphi(x) = \int_a^b f(x, t)dt$$

In this chapter we shall set out to find solutions of differential equations in this form.

The solution will be most manageable if it is the integral of a real function with respect to a real variable, but there are advantages in discussing the problem on the wider basis of complex function-theory and seeking solutions

$$w = \int_C f(z, \zeta)d\zeta,$$

where C is a contour in the ζ-plane.

We make one remark here to save constant repetition throughout the chapter. When an integrand contains a function such as $(\zeta - a)^k$, which is many-valued, it is to be understood that one of its values is fixed for a suitable value of ζ, and that this chosen branch of the function is followed along the contour of integration.

32. Laplace's linear equation. As an example of an equation whose solutions are conveniently expressed as complex integrals, we take the nth order equation

$$(a_n z + b_n)w^{(n)} + \ldots + (a_1 z + b_1)w' + (a_0 z + b_0)w = 0, \quad (32.1)$$

in which the coefficients of w and its derivatives are of the first degree in z. This equation in real variables is discussed by Ince, Text, p. 104.

Try to solve the equation by

$$w = \int_C e^{z\zeta} P(\zeta) d\zeta$$

for a suitable choice of the function $P(\zeta)$ and the contour C. It will be seen in the light of experience why this is a hopeful trial solution. Substitute for w and its derivatives in the equation. We assume that $P(\zeta)$ and C are such that the derivatives are given by differentiating with respect to z under the sign of integration.

The differential equation is satisfied if

$$\int_C e^{z\zeta} P(\zeta)\{z\,Q(\zeta) + R(\zeta)\}d\zeta = 0,$$

where $\qquad Q(\zeta) = a_n \zeta^n + \ldots + a_1 \zeta + a_0$

and $\qquad R(\zeta) = b_n \zeta^n + \ldots + b_1 \zeta + b_0.$

The integrand is an exact derivative

$$\frac{d}{d\zeta}\{e^{z\zeta}S(\zeta)\}$$

if

$$S(\zeta) = P(\zeta)Q(\zeta)$$

and

$$S'(\zeta) = P(\zeta)R(\zeta).$$

So $S(\zeta)$ can be found from

$$\frac{S'(\zeta)}{S(\zeta)} = \frac{R(\zeta)}{Q(\zeta)} = k_0 + \frac{k_1}{\zeta - \alpha_1} + \ldots + \frac{k_n}{\zeta - \alpha_n},$$

where $\alpha_1, \ldots, \alpha_n$ are the zeros of $Q(\zeta)$, assumed for the present all different. So we can take

$$S(\zeta) = e^{k_0 \zeta}(\zeta - \alpha_1)^{k_1} \ldots (\zeta - \alpha_n)^{k_n}$$

and $$P(\zeta) = e^{k_0 \zeta}(\zeta - \alpha_1)^{k_1 - 1} \ldots (\zeta - \alpha_n)^{k_n - 1}.$$

The integral $\int_C \dfrac{d}{d\zeta} \{e^{z\zeta} S(\zeta)\} d\zeta = [e^{z\zeta} S(\zeta)]_C$ and this vanishes if the contour C is chosen so that

$$[\varphi(\zeta)]_C \equiv [e^{(z+k_0)\zeta}(\zeta - \alpha_1)^{k_1} \ldots (\zeta - \alpha_n)^{k_n}]_C = 0.$$

Before embarking on a general discussion of the choice of contours it will be helpful to consider an illustrative example.

Example.

$$zw'' + (p + q + z)w' + pw = 0.$$

Take $w = \int_C e^{z\zeta} P(\zeta) d\zeta$. The reader is advised to carry through the detail for himself, and he will find that

$$\int_C e^{z\zeta} \zeta^{p-1}(\zeta + 1)^{q-1} d\zeta$$

is a solution if

$$[e^{z\zeta} \zeta^p (\zeta + 1)^q]_C = 0.$$

It is convenient to replace ζ by $-\zeta$, and then

$$\int_C e^{-z\zeta} \zeta^{p-1}(1 - \zeta)^{q-1} d\zeta$$

is a solution if

$$[e^{-z\zeta} \zeta^p (1 - \zeta)^q]_C = 0.$$

Suppose for simplicity that z, p, q are real. If $p > 0$ or $q > 0$, the integrated part in square brackets vanishes at $\zeta = 0$ or $\zeta = 1$ respectively. If $z > 0$ or $z < 0$, it vanishes at $\zeta = \infty$ or $\zeta = -\infty$ respectively. We arrive thus at solutions of the equation, of which the following are typical, where C is the interval of the real axis specified.

If $p > 0, q > 0,$ C is $(0, 1)$;

   $p > 0, x < 0,$ C is $(-\infty, 0)$.

If $p < 0, q < 0, x < 0$, no single segment of the real axis meets the requirements for C, but we can take a contour composed of the part of the real axis from $-\infty$ to $-\delta$, then a circle of radius δ and centre the origin, and then returning from $-\delta$ to $-\infty$.

These indications do not profess to give the complete solution of the example, but they lead up to the next section.

33.   Choice of contours.

In the general case of § 32, there are various possible types of contour C. The condition $[\varphi(\zeta)]_C = 0$ is satisfied if C is closed and $\varphi(\zeta)$ returns to its initial value after describing it. In this case, C must contain at least one of the points α_r inside it, for if not it would give only the trivial solution $w = 0$. Another possibility is to make C go to infinity in one or more directions for which $\varphi(\zeta) \to 0$; as $\varphi(\zeta)$ depends on z, these directions will depend on the values of z.

When ζ goes round the point α_1 counter-clockwise the power $(\zeta - \alpha_1)^{k_1}$ is multiplied by $e^{2\pi i k_1}$. We can therefore define a C for which $[\varphi(\zeta)]_C = 0$ by taking a loop round each of α_1 and α_2 twice in opposite directions (a double-loop contour), as shown in the figure.

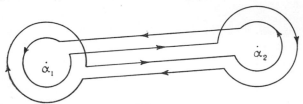

Fig. 1.

For clearness in the diagram, the parts of the contour are drawn out separately; they can in fact be circles described twice round α_1 and α_2 together with segments of the line joining them. By taking double-loop contours round α_1 and each of $\alpha_2, \ldots, \alpha_n$ in turn we obtain $n - 1$ independent solutions of the equation and these solutions have the advantage of being valid for all values of z.

These $n - 1$ solutions may be expected to be independent; a general formal proof of independence (e.g. by the

Wronskian criterion of § 7) would be formidable. If it is possible to deform one contour C_1 continuously into another C_2 without passing over any of the points α_i, then integrals along C_1 and C_2 yield the same solution of the differential equation; if such a deformation is not possible, the values of the integrals are in general different. The reader will see that it is impossible to deform one of the double-loop contours defined in the last paragraph into another without passing over points α_i.

To construct an nth independent solution of the equation valid for given values of z, choose a direction in the ζ plane for which the real part of $(z + k_0)\zeta$ is negative, and take as the contour of integration, say, one coming from infinity in that direction, encircling α_1 (and no other α) and returning to infinity in the same direction. (Fig. 2)

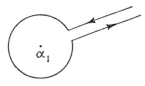

Fig. 2.

It is possible to define each of the n solutions by a contour of this type instead of taking $n - 1$ double-loop contours and only one of this type.

34. Further examples of contours.

General principles governing choice of contours have been laid down in § 33. Some details have still to be clarified — for instance, we have still to show how to find n independent solutions when the α's are not all different. The procedure to be followed will be seen more readily from a study of particular examples than from description in general terms. As a first example it is instructive to see how the technique of § 32 would yield the known solution of the linear equation with constant coefficients.

Example 1.

$$b_n w^{(n)} + \ldots + b_1 w' + b_0 w = 0.$$

We find that $\int_C e^{z\zeta} P(\zeta) d\zeta$ is a solution if

$$\int_C e^{z\zeta} P(\zeta) R(\zeta) d\zeta = 0,$$

where

$$R(\zeta) = b_n \zeta^n + \ldots + b_1 \zeta + b_0.$$

Suppose that $(\zeta - \beta)^r$ is a factor of $R(\zeta)$.

Then

$$\int_C e^{z\zeta} P(\zeta) R(\zeta) d\zeta = 0$$

if $\qquad P(\zeta) = \dfrac{A_r}{(\zeta - \beta)^r} + \ldots + \dfrac{A_1}{\zeta - \beta} + p(\zeta),$

where $p(\zeta)$ is regular at $\zeta = \beta$, and C is a contour enclosing β and no other zero of $R(\zeta)$.

From Cauchy's integral formula,

$$\int_C e^{z\zeta} P(\zeta) d\zeta = e^{z\beta} (B_{r-1} z^{r-1} + \ldots + B_0),$$

where the B's are constants. This gives the r independent solutions corresponding to the r-fold root β.

The next example shows that a double-loop contour encircling two branch-points of $P(\zeta)$ may sometimes be replaced by a simpler contour — a *figure-of-eight* going round the two points in opposite directions.

Example 2.

$$zw'' + (2\nu + 1)w' + zw = 0, \qquad (\nu = \text{constant}).$$

A solution is $\qquad w = \int_C e^{z\zeta} (\zeta^2 + 1)^{\nu - \frac{1}{2}} d\zeta,$

where $\qquad [e^{z\zeta} (\zeta^2 + 1)^{\nu + \frac{1}{2}}]_C = 0.$

This condition is satisfied if C is a figure-of-eight contour, one loop containing $\zeta = i$ and the other $\zeta = -i$, since the factors $\exp\{\pm 2\pi i (\nu + \frac{1}{2})\}$ acquired respectively by $(\zeta - i)^{\nu + \frac{1}{2}}$ and $(\zeta + i)^{\nu + \frac{1}{2}}$ cancel. (We are supposing that ν has not one of the values $\frac{1}{2}, \frac{3}{2}, \frac{5}{2}, \ldots,$ which would give $w \equiv 0$).

In this example, the result is simplified if we change the variable ζ to it, so as to transform $\pm i$ into ± 1.

Then $w = \displaystyle\int_C e^{izt}(1 - t^2)^{\nu-\frac{1}{2}} dt$ is a solution, with the following as possible choices of C.

(i) if $\nu > -\frac{1}{2}$, the straight line from -1 to $+1$, and, if ν has not one of the values $\frac{1}{2}$, $\frac{3}{2}$, $\frac{5}{2}$, . . .,

(ii) a figure-of-eight round -1 and $+1$,

(iii) if z is real and positive, a contour coming from and returning to infinity along the positive imaginary axis and going round -1 and $+1$.

The next example illustrates contours going to infinity in different directions.

Example 3.
$$w'' = zw.$$

(This has been solved in series as Example 1 of § 16). The substitution $w = \displaystyle\int_C e^{z\zeta}P(\zeta)d\zeta$ gives $P(\zeta) = e^{-\frac{1}{3}\zeta^3}$, where C has to satisfy

$$[\varphi(\zeta)]_C \equiv [e^{z\zeta - \frac{1}{3}\zeta^3}]_C = 0.$$

Now (whatever the value of z), $\varphi(\zeta) \to 0$ as ζ tends to infinity with its amplitude lying within any of three sectors, namely $\left(-\dfrac{\pi}{6}, \dfrac{\pi}{6}\right)$, $\left(\dfrac{\pi}{2}, \dfrac{5\pi}{6}\right)$, $\left[\left(-\dfrac{\pi}{2}, -\dfrac{5\pi}{6}\right)\right]$ or S_1, S_2, S_3 say. So we can take as contours C giving independent solutions, e.g. (i) one coming from infinity in S_2 and going to infinity in S_1, (ii) one coming from infinity in S_3 and going to infinity in S_2.

35. Integrals containing a power of $\zeta - z$.

The feature of Laplace's linear equation (32.1) which suits it to solution by integrals of which the 'kernel' is $e^{z\zeta}$ is the linearity in z of the coefficient of each $w^{(r)}$; the integrand resulting from substitution in the given differential equation is an exact first derivative of a function $e^{z\zeta}S(\zeta)$ and the differential equation determining $S(\zeta)$ is of the first order. If the coefficients of $w^{(r)}$ are polynomials of degree m, then we should have to try to express the integrand as an m-th derivative, and the ensuing differential equation for $S(\zeta)$ is of order m, and it may not be easier to solve than the original equation.

It is natural to ask whether contour integrals having kernels of other than exponential form may be of service in solving differential equations. One other useful form is

$$\int_C (\zeta - z)^{\lambda+1} P(\zeta) d\zeta, \qquad (35.1)$$

where λ is a constant to be chosen. We shall show that this form is appropriate to an equation in which the coefficient of $w^{(r)}$ is a polynomial of degree r in z. We shall give the detail for the second-order equation

$$q(z)w'' + l(z)w' + kw = 0, \qquad (35.2)$$

$q(z)$ being quadratic in z, $l(z)$ linear and k a constant.

First we write equation (35.2) in the form

$$\begin{aligned} q(z)w'' - \lambda q'(z)w' + \tfrac{1}{2}\lambda(\lambda + 1)q''(z)w \\ - r(z)w' + (\lambda + 1)r'(z)w = 0. \end{aligned} \qquad (35.3)$$

This is possible because comparison of the coefficients of w' and w in (35.2) and (35.3) determines λ and the linear function $r(z)$. (For the detail see Example, p. 67).

The equation (35.3) is satisfied by the integral (35.1) if

$$\int_C P(\zeta) \begin{bmatrix} \lambda(\lambda+1)(\zeta-z)^{\lambda-1}\{q(z)+(\zeta-z)q'(z)+\tfrac{1}{2}(\zeta-z)^2 q''(z)\} \\ +(\lambda+1)(\zeta-z)^\lambda\{r(z)+(\zeta-z)r'(z)\} \end{bmatrix} d\zeta = 0,$$

that is to say, if

$$\int_C P(\zeta)\{\lambda(\zeta-z)^{\lambda-1}q(\zeta)+(\zeta-z)^\lambda r(\zeta)\}d\zeta = 0.$$

The integrand is

$$\frac{d}{d\zeta}\{S(\zeta)(\zeta - z)^\lambda\}$$

if
$$S(\zeta) = P(\zeta)q(\zeta)$$

and
$$S'(\zeta) = P(\zeta)r(\zeta).$$

So $S(\zeta)$ can be found from

$$\frac{S'(\zeta)}{S(\zeta)} = \frac{r(\zeta)}{q(\zeta)} = \frac{k_1}{\zeta - \alpha_1} + \frac{k_2}{\zeta - \alpha_2}.$$

We thus find that

$$w = \int_C (\zeta - \alpha_1)^{k_1-1}(\zeta - \alpha_2)^{k_2-1}(\zeta - z)^{\lambda+1}d\zeta$$

is a solution of the equation (35.2) if C is chosen so that

$$[(\zeta - \alpha_1)^{k_1}(\zeta - \alpha_2)^{k_2}(\zeta - z)^{\lambda}]_C = 0.$$

The contour C is to be chosen by the principles developed in § 33.

Example.

Apply the above method to the hypergeometric equation (26.1)

$$z(1 - z)w'' + \{c - (a + b + 1)z\}w' - abw = 0.$$

With the notation of the general discussion, we have

$$q(z) = z(1 - z),$$
$$\lambda(1 - 2z) + r(z) = (a + b + 1)z - c,$$
$$\tfrac{1}{2}\lambda(\lambda + 1)(- 2) + (\lambda + 1)r'(z) = - ab$$

Eliminating $r(z)$, we find $\lambda = - a - 1$ or $\lambda = - b - 1$. Taking $\lambda = - a - 1$, we find $r(z) = (a - c + 1) - (a - b + 1)z$. So

$$\frac{S'(\zeta)}{S(\zeta)} = \frac{r(\zeta)}{q(\zeta)} = \frac{a - c + 1}{\zeta} - \frac{c - b}{1 - \zeta}$$

and we have the solution

$$w = \int_C \zeta^{a-c}(1 - \zeta)^{c-b-1}(\zeta - z)^{-a}d\zeta, \qquad (35.4)$$

where C is such that

$$[\zeta^{a-c+1}(1 - \zeta)^{c-b}(\zeta - z)^{-a-1}]_C = 0.$$

C can always be taken to be a double-loop contour round $\zeta = 0$ and $\zeta = 1$ or round $\zeta = 0$ and $\zeta = z$, unless the values of a, b, c are such as to allow a simpler type of contour.

The second value $\lambda = - b - 1$ gives a contour integral solution got by interchanging a and b in (35.4).

If in (35.4) we put $\zeta = 1/\eta$, we obtain

$$w = \int \eta^{b-1} (1 - \eta)^{c-b-1} (1 - z\eta)^{-a} d\eta$$

along an appropriate contour. When $\mathbf{R}c > \mathbf{R}b > 0$, this integral can be taken along the segment $(0, 1)$ of the real axis, and this is the expression already found in § 28.

Examples.

1. Find a solution of the differential equation

$$w'' - 2zw' + 2kw = 0 \qquad (k \geqq 0)$$

of the form $\int_C e^{2z\zeta} f(\zeta) d\zeta$, describing two possible types of contour C. Show that, if k is a positive integer, there is a solution of the form

$$H_k(z) = (-1)^k e^{z^2} \frac{d^k}{dz^k} e^{-z^2}.$$

2. For the equation of example 1, obtain also solutions

$$\int e^{z^2\zeta} \zeta^{-1-\frac{1}{2}k} (1 - \zeta)^{-\frac{1}{2}+\frac{1}{2}k} d\zeta, \qquad z \int e^{z^2\zeta} \zeta^{-\frac{1}{2}-\frac{1}{2}k} (1 - \zeta)^{\frac{1}{2}k} d\zeta$$

along appropriate contours.

3. Find solutions in series of the differential equation

$$y'' - 2xy' + 2\lambda y = 0.$$

Investigate also solutions of the form $\int_C e^{2xt} u(t) dt$, where C is a suitable contour. Show in particular that, if $\lambda < 0$, two solutions are

$$\int_0^\infty e^{-t^2+2xt} t^{-\lambda-1} dt \quad \text{and} \quad \int_{-\infty}^\infty e^{-t^2+2xt} t^{-\lambda-1} dt$$

and recover the solutions in series from these.

4. Prove that the differential equation

$$zw'' + 2aw' - zw = 0,$$

where a is a real constant, may be satisfied by taking

$$w = \int_C (t^2 - 1)^{a-1} e^{tz} dt,$$

where C is a suitable contour. Show, in particular, that possible forms of contour are

(i) a figure of eight encircling the points $t = 1$ and $t = -1$ in opposite directions;

(ii) a path coming along the negative real axis from $-\infty$ and returning to $-\infty$ along the negative real axis after encircling the point $t = -1$, provided that $\mathbf{R}z > 0$;

(iii) the real axis from $t = -1$ to $t = 1$, provided that $a > 0$;

(iv) the real axis from $-\infty$ to -1, provided that $a > 0$ and $\mathbf{R}z > 0$.

Show that, when the stated conditions are satisfied, the solution given by (ii) is a constant multiple of that given by (iv). Verify that, when $a = 0$, the contours (i) and (ii) give two linearly independent solutions.

5. Show that the equation

$$D^n y - xy = 0$$

is satisfied by

$$y = \sum_{r=0}^{n} A_r \omega^r \int_0^\infty \exp\left\{\omega^r xt - \frac{t^{n+1}}{n+1}\right\} dt,$$

where $\omega = \exp\{2\pi i/(n+1)\}$ and $\sum_{r=0}^{n} A_r = 0$.

6. Prove that the equation

$$zw'' + cw' - w = 0$$

has solutions of the form

$$\int e^{z\zeta + 1/\zeta}\, \zeta^{c-2}\, d\zeta, \qquad z^{1-c} \int e^{z\zeta + 1/\zeta}\, \zeta^{-c}\, d\zeta,$$

specifying the appropriate contours.

7. Obtain the complete solution in contour integrals of the equation

$$zw''' + w = 0.$$

Examples 1, 4, 7, 18 of Chapter IV are also suitable for solution by contour integrals.

CHAPTER VII

LEGENDRE FUNCTIONS

36. Genesis of Legendre's equation. Many problems of mathematical physics involve the finding of a function V which satisfies Laplace's equation

$$\frac{\partial^2 V}{\partial x^2} + \frac{\partial^2 V}{\partial y^2} + \frac{\partial^2 V}{\partial z^2} = 0$$

and also satisfies certain boundary conditions (for example, if V is electrostatic potential, it is constant on the surface of a conductor). Any simplifying feature of the problem specialises the form of solution of Laplace's equation that has to be found. We shall suppose in what follows that there is symmetry about a line, which is taken to be the z-axis.

Laplace's equation transformed to spherical polar coordinates

$$x = r \sin\theta \cos\varphi, \quad y = r \sin\theta \sin\varphi, \quad z = r \cos\theta$$

is

$$\frac{\partial^2 V}{\partial r^2} + \frac{2}{r}\frac{\partial V}{\partial r} + \frac{1}{r^2}\frac{\partial^2 V}{\partial \theta^2} + \frac{\cot\theta}{r^2}\frac{\partial V}{\partial \theta} + \frac{1}{r^2 \sin^2\theta}\frac{\partial^2 V}{\partial \varphi^2} = 0.$$

We are then interested in solutions which are independent of φ. Putting $V = r^n \Theta$, where Θ is a function of θ only, so that V is homogeneous and of degree n, we find

$$\frac{d^2\Theta}{d\theta^2} + \cot\theta \frac{d\Theta}{d\theta} + n(n+1)\Theta = 0,$$

or, changing the independent variable to $\mu = \cos\theta$,

$$(1 - \mu^2)\frac{d^2\Theta}{d\mu^2} - 2\mu \frac{d\Theta}{d\mu} + n(n+1)\Theta = 0,$$

a second-order equation for Θ as a function of μ. This is Legendre's equation.

In physical applications Θ and μ are real and $-1 \leqq \mu \leqq 1$. In investigating the functions which are defined as solutions of the equation, we get a more comprehensive picture if the variables are complex, and we replace Θ, μ, by w, z, obtaining

$$(1 - z^2)w'' - 2zw' + n(n + 1)w = 0, \qquad (36.1)$$

an equation with regular singularities at -1, 1, ∞.

37. Legendre polynomials.

It will be shown that, if n is a positive integer or zero, Legendre's equation (36.1) has a polynomial solution of degree n. The coefficients of powers of z in the polynomial are found most readily if we solve in series of powers of $1/z$. Write

$$w = \frac{1}{z^\rho}\Big(c_0 + \frac{c_1}{z} + \ldots + \frac{c_r}{z^r} + \ldots\Big).$$

Substituting in the equation and equating coefficients of $z^{-\rho}$, we have the indicial equation

$$-\rho(\rho + 1) + 2\rho + n(n + 1) = 0,$$

giving $\rho = n + 1$ or $\rho = -n$.

We obtain the recurrence relation

$$c_r(\rho + r + n)(\rho + r - n - 1) = c_{r-2}(\rho + r - 1)(\rho + r - 2).$$

The exponent $\rho = -n$ gives the solution

$$w = Az^n\Big\{1 - \frac{n(n-1)}{2(2n-1)}z^{-2} + \frac{n(n-1)(n-2)(n-3)}{2 \cdot 4(2n-1)(2n-3)}z^{-4} - \ldots\Big\}.$$

This is a polynomial of degree n.

We define $P_n(z)$ to be the value of w when

$$A = \frac{(2n)!}{2^n(n!)^2},$$

so that

$$P_n(z) = \frac{1}{2^n} \sum_{r=0}^{p} \frac{(-1)^r (2n - 2r)!}{r!(n-r)!(n-2r)!} z^{n-2r}, \qquad (37.1)$$

where p is $\frac{1}{2}n$ or $\frac{1}{2}(n-1)$ according as n is even or odd. If will be seen later that this choice of the constant A makes $P_n(1) = 1$.

Since $0 \leqq 2n - 2r < n$ when $p + 1 \leqq r \leqq n$ it follows that $\dfrac{d^n}{dz^n} z^{2n-2r}$ vanishes when $p + 1 \leqq r \leqq n$. Consequently the expression (37.1) for $P_n(z)$ gives

$$\begin{aligned}
P_n(z) &= \frac{1}{2^n} \sum_{r=0}^{n} \frac{(-1)^r}{r!(n-r)!} \frac{d^n}{dz^n} z^{2n-2r} \\
&= \frac{1}{2^n n!} \frac{d^n}{dz^n} \sum_{r=0}^{n} \frac{(-1)^r n!}{r!(n-r)!} z^{2n-2r} \\
&= \frac{1}{2^n n!} \frac{d^n}{dz^n} (z^2 - 1)^n. \qquad (37.2)
\end{aligned}$$

The formula (37.2) is known as **Rodrigues' formula.**

38. Integrals for $P_n(z)$.

Apply Cauchy's formula for the nth derivative of a regular function (Phillips, Text, p. 95)

$$\frac{d^n}{dz^n} f(z) = \frac{n!}{2\pi i} \int_C \frac{f(\zeta) d\zeta}{(\zeta - z)^{n+1}}$$

to Rodrigues' formula for $P_n(z)$ and we have **Schläfli's integral**

$$P_n(z) = \frac{1}{2\pi i} \int_C \frac{(\zeta^2 - 1)^n d\zeta}{2^n (\zeta - z)^{n+1}}, \qquad (38.1)$$

where C is a contour enclosing $\zeta = z$.

We shall show how Schläfli's integral can be transformed into one in which the variable of integration is real.

Take C to be the circle with centre z and radius $|z^2 - 1|^{\frac{1}{2}}$.

Then on this contour C we have

$$\zeta = z + (z^2 - 1)^{1/2} e^{i\varphi}, \quad (-\pi < \varphi \leqq \pi),$$
$$\zeta^2 - 1 = (z^2 - 1)(1 + e^{2i\varphi}) + 2z(z^2 - 1)^{1/2} e^{i\varphi}$$
$$= 2(z^2 - 1)^{1/2} e^{i\varphi}\{z + (z^2 - 1)^{1/2} \cos \varphi\}.$$

Substitute in Schläfli's integral and we have

$$P_n(z) = \frac{1}{2\pi} \int_{-\pi}^{\pi} \{z + (z^2 - 1)^{1/2} \cos \varphi\}^n d\varphi,$$

or, since the integrand is an even function of φ,

$$P_n(z) = \frac{1}{\pi} \int_{0}^{\pi} \{z + (z^2 - 1)^{1/2} \cos \varphi\}^n d\varphi. \quad (38.2)$$

The formula (38.2) is **Laplace's integral** for $P_n(z)$.

In the foregoing argument it is indifferent which branch of $(z^2 - 1)^{1/2}$ is chosen.

39.　The generating function. Recurrence relations.

THEOREM 20. *If $|h|$ is sufficiently small, and if $(1 - 2zh + h^2)^{\frac{1}{2}}$ takes that value which is $+1$ when $h = 0$, then*

$$\frac{1}{(1 - 2zh + h^2)^{1/2}} = 1 + hP_1(z) + \ldots + h^n P_n(z) + \ldots \quad (39.1)$$

PROOF. Laplace's integral (38.2) for $P_n(z)$ gives

$$\sum_{n=0}^{\infty} h^n P_n(z) = \frac{1}{\pi} \sum_{n=0}^{\infty} \int_{0}^{\pi} h^n\{(z + (z^2 - 1)^{1/2} \cos \varphi\}^n d\varphi.$$

If now

$$|h|\{|z| + |z^2 - 1|^{1/2}\} \leqq k < 1,$$

the geometrical progression

$$\sum_{n=0}^{\infty} h^n(z + (z^2 - 1)^{1/2} \cos \varphi\}^n$$

converges uniformly with respect to φ. It may therefore be integrated term-by-term with respect to φ giving

$$\sum_{n=0}^{\infty} h^n P_n(z) = \frac{1}{\pi} \int_0^\pi \frac{d\varphi}{1 - hz - h(z^2 - 1)^{\frac{1}{2}} \cos \varphi}.$$

The integral on the right-hand side is an elementary one whose value is $\pi(1 - 2zh + h^2)^{-\frac{1}{2}}$ and so we have proved that

$$\sum_{n=0}^{\infty} h^n P_n(z) = \frac{1}{(1 - 2zh + h^2)^{\frac{1}{2}}}.$$

To obtain a recurrence relation connecting consecutive $P_n(z)$, differentiate the last equation with respect to h and we obtain

$$(1 - 2zh + h^2) \sum_{n=0}^{\infty} nh^{n-1} P_n(z) = (z - h) \sum_{n=0}^{\infty} h^n P_n(z).$$

Equate coefficients of h^{n-1} and we have

$$nP_n(z) - (2n - 1)zP_{n-1}(z) + (n - 1)P_{n-2}(z) = 0 \quad (39.2)$$

Again, differentiating the generating function and the series, we find that

$$h \sum_{n=0}^{\infty} nh^{n-1} P_n(z) = (z - h) \sum_{n=0}^{\infty} h^n P_n'(z),$$

and so, by equating coefficients of h^n,

$$zP_n'(z) - P_{n-1}'(z) = nP_n(z).$$

From these recurrence relations a number of others can be obtained.

40. The function $P_\nu(z)$ for general ν. Put ν for n in Schläfli's integral (38.1), and write

$$w = \frac{1}{2\pi i} \int_c \frac{(\zeta^2 - 1)^\nu d\zeta}{2^\nu (\zeta - z)^{\nu+1}},$$

specifying the branches of the many-valued functions.

The contour C will be defined in a moment. With the above value of w, we find that

$$(1 - z^2)w'' - 2zw' + \nu(\nu + 1)w$$

$$= \frac{\nu + 1}{2\pi i \cdot 2^\nu} \int_C \frac{d}{d\zeta} \left\{ \frac{(\zeta^2 - 1)^{\nu+1}}{(\zeta - z)^{\nu+2}} \right\} d\zeta$$

$$= \frac{\nu + 1}{2\pi i \cdot 2^\nu} \left[\frac{(\zeta^2 - 1)^{\nu+1}}{(\zeta - z)^{\nu+2}} \right]_C.$$

We have therefore a solution of Legendre's equation if C is such that the expression in square brackets returns to its initial value. Possible choices of C are

(i) A simple contour containing $\zeta = 1$ and $\zeta = z$, but not $\zeta = -1$,

(ii) A figure of eight round $\zeta = -1$ and $\zeta = 1$, not containing $\zeta = z$.

These contours are not deformable into one another and the functions defined by them are independent. The choice (i) for C defines $w = P_\nu(z)$.

Taking (ii) for C, we define the resulting solution of Legendre's equation to be a multiple $(4i \sin \nu\pi)$ of $Q_\nu(z)$. For an account of the properties of the function $Q_\nu(z)$, as well as for further discussion of $P_\nu(z)$, the reader is referred to Sneddon's Text, *The Special Functions of Physics and Chemistry*.

Examples.

1. From Rodrigues' formula prove by integration by parts that

$$\int_{-1}^{1} P_m(x)P_n(x)dx = 0 \quad (m \neq n).$$

Prove also (i) from Rodrigues' formula, (ii) from the generating function, that

$$\int_{-1}^{1} P_n^2(x)dx = \frac{2}{2n + 1}.$$

This example illustrates the fact that there is a sense in which the numbers $\lambda = n(n + 1)$ are the eigenvalues of the equation

$$(1 - x^2)y'' - 2xy' + \lambda y = 0$$

for the interval $(-1, 1)$, the $P_n(x)$ being the corresponding eigen-functions. But this fact does not follow from the theorems given in Chapter III without further discussion, because $x = -1$ and $x = 1$ are singularities of the equation.

2. Express $P_n(z)$ as the hypergeometric function

$$F(n + 1, -n; 1; \tfrac{1}{2} - \tfrac{1}{2}z).$$

3. Prove that the second solution of Legendre's equation in the neighbourhood of $z = \infty$ is

$$Az^{-n-1}F(\tfrac{1}{2}n + \tfrac{1}{2}, \tfrac{1}{2}n + 1; n + \tfrac{3}{2}; z^{-2}).$$

Calling $Q_n(z)$ the value of this function when $A = \dfrac{n!\sqrt{\pi}}{2^{n+1}\Gamma\left(n + \tfrac{3}{2}\right)}$, prove that

$$Q_n(z) = \frac{1}{(2z)^{n+1}} \int_{-1}^{1} (1 - t^2)^n \left(1 - \frac{t}{z}\right)^{-n-1} dt.$$

4. Legendre's equation being of the type discussed in § 35, use that method to obtain the integral of § 40.

CHAPTER VIII

BESSEL FUNCTIONS

41. Genesis of Bessel's equation. In § 22 we used Bessel's equation

$$z^2 w'' + z w' + (z^2 - v^2)w = 0 \qquad (41.1)$$

to illustrate solution in series. The equation has a regular singularity at $z = 0$ and an irregular singularity at $z = \infty$.

We show how Bessel's equation emerges from physical problems. The wave-equation, with x, y, z as Cartesian coordinates and t as time, is

$$\frac{\partial^2 V}{\partial x^2} + \frac{\partial^2 V}{\partial y^2} + \frac{\partial^2 V}{\partial z^2} = \frac{1}{c^2} \frac{\partial^2 V}{\partial t^2}.$$

In cylindrical coordinates with $x = r \cos\theta$, $y = r \sin\theta$, the equation is

$$\frac{\partial^2 V}{\partial r^2} + \frac{1}{r} \frac{\partial V}{\partial r} + \frac{1}{r^2} \frac{\partial^2 V}{\partial \theta^2} + \frac{\partial^2 V}{\partial z^2} = \frac{1}{c^2} \frac{\partial^2 V}{\partial t^2}.$$

Seek solutions of the form †

$$V = R(r)\Theta(\theta)Z(z)T(t),$$

where, by the method of separation of variables, R, Θ, Z, T satisfy the equations

$$\frac{d^2 R}{dr^2} + \frac{1}{r} \frac{dR}{dr} - \frac{m^2}{r^2} R + n^2 R = 0,$$

$$\frac{d^2 \Theta}{d\theta^2} = -m^2 \Theta,$$

$$\frac{d^2 Z}{dz^2} = -q^2 Z,$$

$$\frac{d^2 T}{dt^2} = -c^2 p^2 T, \quad n^2 = p^2 - q^2.$$

† C. A. Coulson, *Waves*, p. 10.

For the solution to be single-valued, m must be an integer.

The equation for R is Bessel's equation as quoted at the beginning of this chapter, when w, z, ν are written for R, nr, m respectively.

As an application of the wave-equation, consider vibrations of a circular membrane of radius a, the boundary $r = a$ being clamped. Then we shall need solutions $R(r)$ which vanish for $r = a$; therefore a knowledge of the zeros of solutions of Bessel's equation will be of importance.

42. The solution $J_\nu(z)$ in series. From the work on page 43, if ν is not a negative integer,

$$w = c_0 z^\nu \left\{ 1 - \frac{(\tfrac{1}{2}z)^2}{1 \cdot (\nu + 1)} + \frac{(\tfrac{1}{2}z)^4}{1 \cdot 2 \cdot (\nu + 1)(\nu + 2)} - \cdots \right\}$$

is a solution of Bessel's equation (41.1). It is convenient to take $c_0 = 1/2^\nu \Gamma(\nu + 1)$ and define

$$J_\nu(z) = (\tfrac{1}{2}z)^\nu \sum_{r=0}^{\infty} \frac{(-1)^r (\tfrac{1}{2}z)^{2r}}{r! \, \Gamma(\nu + r + 1)} \qquad (42.1)$$

as the Bessel function of order ν. If ν is not an integer, the branch of the many-valued function $(\tfrac{1}{2}z)^\nu$ needs to be specified and is taken to be $\exp(\nu \log \tfrac{1}{2}z)$, the logarithm having its principal value.

The series for $J_\nu(z)/(\tfrac{1}{2}z)^\nu$ converges for all values of z and is a regular function.

The value of c_0 chosen gives a meaning to $J_\nu(z)$ when ν is a negative integer $-n$, and we have

$$[J_{-n}(z)]^n = (\tfrac{1}{2}z)^{-n} \sum_{r=n}^{\infty} \frac{(-1)^r (\tfrac{1}{2}z)^{2r}}{r! \, \Gamma(-n + r + 1)}.$$

Now $1/\Gamma(t)$ vanishes when t is a negative integer or zero, and so

$$J_{-n}(z) = (\tfrac{1}{2}z)^{-n} \sum_{r=0}^{\infty} \frac{(-1)^r (\tfrac{1}{2}z)^{2r}}{r! \, \Gamma(-n + r + 1)}$$

$$= (\tfrac{1}{2}z)^n \sum_{s=0}^{\infty} \frac{(-1)^{n+s} (\tfrac{1}{2}z)^{2s}}{\Gamma(n + s + 1) s!} = (-1)^n J_n(z).$$

When ν is not an integer or zero, the functions $J_\nu(z)$ and $J_{-\nu}(z)$ are linearly independent, and the complete solution of Bessel's equation is

$$AJ_\nu(z) + BJ_{-\nu}(z).$$

As we have seen, however, it is the value $\nu = n$ which is likely to be of physical interest; in this case we have found only one solution $J_n(z)$ and a second solution, if required, can be found by the method of § 20.

We observe that, for $\nu = \pm \frac{1}{2}$,

$$J_{\frac{1}{2}}(z) = \left(\frac{2}{\pi z}\right)^{\frac{1}{2}} \sin z, \quad J_{-\frac{1}{2}}(z) = \left(\frac{2}{\pi z}\right)^{\frac{1}{2}} \cos z.$$

43. The generating function for $J_n(z)$. Recurrence relations.

THEOREM 21. *If* $u \neq 0$, *then*

$$\exp\left\{\left(u - \frac{1}{u}\right)\frac{z}{2}\right\} = \sum_{-\infty}^{\infty} u^n J_n(z). \tag{43.1}$$

PROOF. If z is given, the left-hand side is a regular function of the complex variable u except for $u = 0$ or ∞. It can be expanded in a Laurent series (Phillips, Text, p. 97), absolutely and uniformly convergent for $0 < u_0 \leq u \leq u_1$.

The left-hand side $e^{uz/2} e^{-z/2u}$ takes the form

$$\left(1 + \frac{uz}{2} + \ldots + \frac{u^n z^n}{2^n n!} + \ldots\right)\left(1 - \frac{z}{2u} + \ldots + (-1)^n \frac{z^n}{2^n u^n n!} + \ldots\right).$$

These absolutely convergent series can be multiplied and the product arranged as a Laurent series in u. The coefficient of u^n in the product is, if $n \geq 0$,

$$\frac{z^n}{2^n n!}\left\{1 - \frac{1}{(n+1)}\left(\frac{z}{2}\right)^2 + \frac{1}{2!(n+1)(n+2)}\left(\frac{z}{2}\right)^4 - \ldots\right\} = J_n(z),$$

and, if n is a negative integer $- m$, the coefficient of u^n is

$$J_m(-z) = (-1)^m J_m(z) = J_{-m}(z).$$

The generating function (43.1) yields recurrence relations. Differentiating term-by-term with respect to u, we find

$$\left(1 + \frac{1}{u^2}\right)\frac{z}{2} \Sigma\, u^n J_n(z) = \Sigma\, n u^{n-1} J_n(z),$$

and so, equating coefficients of u^{n-1},

$$\frac{z}{2}\{J_{n+1}(z) + J_{n-1}(z)\} = n J_n(z). \qquad (43.2)$$

Similarly, from differentiation with respect to z,

$$\tfrac{1}{2}\{J_{n-1}(z) - J_{n+1}(z)\} = J_n'(z). \qquad (43.3)$$

These formulae, suggested most readily by the generating function, could be proved directly from the series for the Bessel functions. This alternative method of proof holds whether the orders of the Bessel functions are integers or not.

Examples.

1. Prove that

$$\{J_0(z)\}^2 + 2\sum_1^\infty \{J_n(z)\}^2 = 1.$$

Deduce that, for real x,

$$|J_0(x)| \leqq 1, \quad |J_n(x)| \leqq \frac{1}{\sqrt{2}}.$$

2. Prove that

$$z J_\nu'(z) = \nu J_\nu(z) - z J_{\nu+1}(z),$$
$$z J_{\nu+1}'(z) = z J_\nu(z) - (\nu+1) J_{\nu+1}(z).$$

Deduce that

$$\frac{J_{\nu+1}(z)}{z^\nu} = -\frac{d}{dz}\left\{\frac{J_\nu(z)}{z^\nu}\right\} \text{ and } z^{\nu+1} J_\nu(z) = \frac{d}{dz}\{z^{\nu+1} J_{\nu+1}(z)\}.$$

44. Integrals for $J_\nu(z)$.

If ν is an integer n, we have a formula due to Bessel,

THEOREM 22. $J_n(z) = \dfrac{1}{\pi} \displaystyle\int_0^\pi \cos(n\theta - z \sin\theta) d\theta.$ (44.1)

PROOF. Take the Laurent expansion of the generating function, divide each side by u^{n+1}, and integrate round the unit circle in the u plane, putting $u = e^{i\theta}$. Thus

$$J_n(z) = \frac{1}{2\pi i} \int \exp\left\{\left(u - \frac{1}{u}\right)\frac{z}{2}\right\} u^{-n-1} du$$

$$= \frac{1}{2\pi} \int_{-\pi}^\pi e^{iz\sin\theta - in\theta} d\theta$$

$$= \frac{1}{2\pi} \int_0^\pi (e^{-in\theta + iz\sin\theta} + e^{in\theta - iz\sin\theta}) d\theta$$

$$= \frac{1}{\pi} \int_0^\pi \cos(n\theta - z\sin\theta) d\theta.$$

A formula valid for more general values of ν is the following.

THEOREM 23. *If $\nu > -\frac{1}{2}$, then*

$$J_\nu(z) = \frac{1}{\Gamma(\nu + \frac{1}{2})\Gamma(\frac{1}{2})}\left(\frac{z}{2}\right)^\nu \int_0^\pi \cos(z\cos\theta)\sin^{2\nu}\theta \, d\theta. \quad (44.2)$$

PROOF. The expansion $\displaystyle\int_0^\pi \cos(z\cos\theta)\sin^{2\nu}\theta \, d\theta$

$$= \int_0^\pi \left\{1 - \frac{z^2\cos^2\theta}{2!} + \ldots + (-1)^r \frac{z^{2r}\cos^{2r}\theta}{(2r)!} + \ldots\right\} \sin^{2\nu}\theta \, d\theta$$

is uniformly convergent for $|z| \leq K$ where K is arbitrarily large, and so integration term-by-term is valid for all finite values of z. Now (by putting $\sin^2\theta = s$)

$$\int_0^\pi \cos^{2r}\theta \sin^{2\nu}\theta d\theta = 2 \int_0^{\frac{1}{2}\pi} \cos^{2r}\theta \sin^{2\nu}\theta \, d\theta$$

$$= \int_0^1 (1 - s)^{r - \frac{1}{2}} s^{\nu - \frac{1}{2}} ds$$

$$= \frac{\Gamma(\nu + \frac{1}{2})\Gamma(r + \frac{1}{2})}{\Gamma(\nu + r + 1)}.$$

Therefore

$$\frac{1}{\Gamma(\nu + \tfrac{1}{2})\Gamma(\tfrac{1}{2})} \left(\frac{z}{2}\right)^\nu \int_0^\pi \cos\,(z \cos \theta) \sin\,^{2\nu} \theta\, d\theta$$

$$= \frac{1}{\Gamma(\tfrac{1}{2})} \left(\frac{z}{2}\right)^\nu \sum_{r=0}^\infty (-1)^r \frac{\Gamma(r + \tfrac{1}{2})}{\Gamma(\nu + r + 1)} \frac{z^{2r}}{(2r)!}$$

$$= \left(\frac{z}{2}\right)^\nu \sum_{r=0}^\infty (-1)^r \frac{(2r - 1)(2r - 3)\ldots 1}{2^r \Gamma(\nu + r + 1)} \frac{z^{2r}}{(2r)!} = J_\nu(z).$$

This formula for $J_\nu(z)$ that we have established can be put into other forms by simple transformations, e.g., putting $\cos \theta = t$, we have, if $\nu > -\tfrac{1}{2}$,

$$J_\nu(z) = \frac{1}{\Gamma(\nu + \tfrac{1}{2})\Gamma(\tfrac{1}{2})} \left(\frac{z}{2}\right)^\nu \int_{-1}^1 (1 - t^2)^{\nu - \frac{1}{2}} \cos zt\, dt. \quad (44.3)$$

In the integrand we can replace $\cos zt$ by e^{izt}.

Integrals of this type can be obtained as special cases of contour integral solutions, and we now show how such solutions may be found.

45. Contour integrals. If in Bessel's equation we write $w = z^\nu W$, the equation for W is found to be

$$zW'' + (2\nu + 1)W' + zW = 0,$$

which is Example 2 of § 34. From the discussion of that example, it follows that

$$J_\nu(z) = Az^\nu \int_C e^{iz\zeta}(1 - \zeta^2)^{\nu - \frac{1}{2}} d\zeta,$$

where C is a contour of one of the types specified there, and A is a constant. If $\nu > -\tfrac{1}{2}$, C can be taken to be the segment $(-1, 1)$ of the real axis as in § 44; more generally, a figure-of-eight or an infinite contour will serve.

46. Application of oscillation theorems. In this section the variables are real. Bessel's equation

$$x^2y'' + xy' + (x^2 - \nu^2)y = 0$$

is reduced to normal form by the substitution $y = vx^{-\frac{1}{2}}$, giving

$$v'' + \left(1 - \frac{4\nu^2 - 1}{4x^2}\right)v = 0.$$

This equation is then satisfied by $v = x^{\frac{1}{2}}J_\nu(x)$. Since the coefficient of v tends to 1 as $x \to \infty$, theorem 13 of § 12 gives at once

THEOREM 24. *If α_r is the rth positive zero of $J_\nu(x)$, then, as $r \to \infty$,*

$$\text{(i)}\ \ \alpha_{r+1} - \alpha_r \sim \pi,$$

and　　　　$$\text{(ii)}\ \ \alpha_r \sim r\pi.$$

The next result uses only Rolle's theorem and makes no appeal to the work of Chapter III.

THEOREM 25. *The zeros of $J_\nu(x)$ and $J_{\nu+1}(x)$, other than $x = 0$, interlace.*

PROOF. The relation

$$\frac{J_{\nu+1}(x)}{x^\nu} = -\frac{d}{dx}\left\{\frac{J_\nu(x)}{x^\nu}\right\}$$

(see § 43, example 2), deducible from the generating function, shows, by Rolle's theorem, that between two zeros of $J_\nu(x)/x^\nu$ lies at least one of $J_{\nu+1}(x)/x^\nu$.

Similarly the other result of the same example

$$x^{\nu+1}J_\nu(x) = \frac{d}{dx}\{x^{\nu+1}J_{\nu+1}(x)\}$$

shows that between two zeros of $x^{\nu+1}J_{\nu+1}(x)$ lies at least one of $x^{\nu+1}J_\nu(x)$.

Since the zeros of $J_\nu(x)$ and $J_{\nu+1}(x)$, other than $x = 0$, are the zeros of the functions discussed in the last two paragraphs, the theorem follows.

We next apply the ideas of § 13 and § 14 about eigen-values and eigenfunctions.

The function

$$u(x) = x^{\frac{1}{2}} J_\nu(\lambda x) \qquad (46.1)$$

satisfies the equation

$$u'' + \left(\lambda^2 - \frac{4\nu^2 - 1}{4x^2}\right) u = 0.$$

Consider solutions which vanish at $x = 0$ and $x = 1$. If $\nu > -\frac{1}{2}$, $u(0) = 0$ for all λ. The vanishing of $u(1)$ means that $J_\nu(\lambda) = 0$, that is to say, the eigenvalues are the zeros of the Bessel function.

If λ_m, λ_n are two values of λ (not necessarily eigen-values) and $u_m(x)$, $u_n(x)$ the corresponding functions as defined by (46.1), then

$$u_m'' + \left(\lambda_m^2 - \frac{4\nu^2 - 1}{4x^2}\right) u_m = 0,$$

$$u_n'' + \left(\lambda_n^2 - \frac{4\nu^2 - 1}{4x^2}\right) u_n = 0.$$

Multiply these equations respectively by u_n, u_m, and subtract. Then integrating from 0 to 1 we have

$$[u_m'(x)u_n(x) - u_m(x)u_n'(x)]_0^1 = (\lambda_n^2 - \lambda_m^2) \int_0^1 u_m u_n dx. \quad (46.2)$$

If $\nu > -\frac{1}{2}$, the expression in square brackets on the left-hand side of (46.2) vanishes for $x = 0$. It also vanishes for $x = 1$ if λ_m and λ_n are eigenvalues. So, if $m \neq n$, we have from (46.2)

$$\int_0^1 u_m u_n dx = 0,$$

and therefore

$$\int_0^1 x J_\nu(\lambda_m x) J_\nu(\lambda_n x) dx = 0 \quad (m \neq n).$$

To evaluate this integral for $m = n$, let λ_n be the nth eigenvalue and in (46.2) replace λ_m by a continuous variable λ_μ taking values tending to λ_n.

Then the equation (46.2) gives

$$(\lambda_n^2 - \lambda_\mu^2) \int_0^1 u_\mu u_n dx = -u_\mu(1) u_n'(1)$$
$$= - J_\nu(\lambda_\mu) \lambda_n J_\nu'(\lambda_n).$$

But, as $\lambda_\mu \to \lambda_n$,

$$\frac{- J_\nu(\lambda_\mu)}{\lambda_n - \lambda_\mu} \to J_\nu'(\lambda_n).$$

And so

$$\int_0^1 x J_\nu^2(\lambda_n x) dx = \int_0^1 u_n^2 dx = \tfrac{1}{2}\{J_\nu'(\lambda_n)\}^2.$$

Examples.

1. By writing $w = vz^{\frac{1}{2}}$, transform the equation

$$\frac{d^2w}{dz^2} + c^2 w = \frac{k(k+1)}{z^2} w$$

into one of Bessel's type and write down its solution.

2. Prove that the equation

$$w'' + zw = 0$$

can be solved by Bessel functions of order $\pm \tfrac{1}{3}$.

3. Prove that Bessel's equation may be written in either of the forms

$$\left\{\frac{d}{dx} + \frac{\nu+1}{x}\right\} \left\{\frac{d}{dx} - \frac{\nu}{x}\right\} y + y = 0,$$
$$\left\{\frac{d}{dx} - \frac{\nu-1}{x}\right\} \left\{\frac{d}{dx} + \frac{\nu}{x}\right\} y + y = 0.$$

Hence show that

$$J_{\nu+1}(x) = - \left(\frac{d}{dx} - \frac{\nu}{x}\right) J_\nu(x),$$
$$J_{\nu-1}(x) = \left(\frac{d}{dx} + \frac{\nu}{x}\right) J_\nu(x),$$

4. Prove that

$$J_n(x) = (-1)^n x^n \left(\frac{1}{x}\frac{d}{dx}\right)^n J_0(x),$$

$$J_{k+n}(x) = (-1)^n x^{k+n} \left(\frac{1}{x}\frac{d}{dx}\right)^n \{x^{-k}J_k(x)\},$$

$$J_{k-n}(x) = x^{n-k} \left(\frac{1}{x}\frac{d}{dx}\right)^n \{x^k J_k(x)\}.$$

5. Prove that, if $a > 0$, $\mu + \nu > 0$,

$$\int_0^\infty e^{-at} J_\nu(bt) t^{\mu-1} dt = \frac{b^\nu \Gamma(\mu+\nu)}{2^\nu (a^2+b^2)^{\frac{1}{2}(\mu+\nu)} \Gamma(\nu+1)} \, F\left(\frac{\mu+\nu}{2}, \frac{1-\mu+\nu}{2}; \nu+1; \frac{b^2}{a^2+b^2}\right).$$

Deduce the value of

$$\int_0^\infty e^{-at} J_0(bt) dt.$$

6. If $\nu + \frac{1}{2} > \mu + \nu > 0$, prove by making a tend to 0 in example 5 that

$$\int_0^\infty J_\nu(t) t^{\mu-1} dt = \frac{2^{\mu-1} \Gamma(\frac{1}{2}\mu + \frac{1}{2}\nu)}{\Gamma(\frac{1}{2}\nu - \frac{1}{2}\mu + 1)}.$$

(It may be assumed that, for large values of t, $|J_\nu(t)| < Kt^{-\frac{1}{2}}$, where K is a constant. This will be proved in § 49.)

CHAPTER IX

ASYMPTOTIC SERIES

47. Asymptotic series. An asymptotic series is a series which, though divergent, is such that the sum of a suitable number of terms yields a good approximation to the function which it represents. The idea is most readily grasped from an example.

Example.

Find an approximation for large positive values of x to the solution of the equation

$$y' - y = -\frac{1}{x}$$

which tends to 0 as $x \to \infty$.

The equation has an irregular singularity at infinity. If we carry out the process of finding a series in powers of $1/x$, we obtain

$$y = \frac{1}{x} - \frac{1}{x^2} + \frac{2!}{x^3} - \ldots + (-1)^{n-1}\frac{(n-1)!}{x^n} + \ldots,$$

which diverges for all values of x.

The equation, being linear and of the first order, can be integrated by a quadrature, and the solution which tends to 0 as $x \to \infty$ is found to be

$$y = f(x) = \int_x^\infty \frac{e^{x-t}}{t}\, dt.$$

If we integrate this expression for $f(x)$ by parts, we see its relation to the divergent series. We have, after n integrations by parts,

$$f(x) = \frac{1}{x} - \frac{1}{x^2} + \frac{2!}{x^3} - \ldots + (-1)^{n-1}\frac{(n-1)!}{x^n} + (-1)^n n! \int_x^\infty \frac{e^{x-t}}{t^{n+1}}\, dt.$$

Now

$$n! \int_x^\infty \frac{e^{x-t}}{t^{n+1}}\, dt < \frac{n!}{x^{n+1}} \int_x^\infty e^{x-t} dt = \frac{n!}{x^{n+1}}.$$

So *the sum of n terms of the series is an approximation to f(x) with an error less than the numerical value of the* $(n + 1)^{th}$ *term.*

For a given value of x the terms of the series decrease in absolute magnitude until the nth term where n is the integer next less than x. If x is large, we can, by stopping at an early term in the series, obtain an approximation of high accuracy. (If x is only 20, the sum of 4 terms gives $f(x)$ with an error less than $1/10^5$.)

48.   Definition and properties of asymptotic series.
The formal definition of an asymptotic series was given by Poincaré (1886).

Let $S_n(z)$ *be the sum of the first* $(n + 1)$ *terms of the series*

$$S(z) = A_0 + \frac{A_1}{z} + \ldots + \frac{A_n}{z^n} + \ldots,$$

Let $R_n(z) = f(z) - S_n(z)$. *Then, for a given range of* arg z, *say* $\alpha \leqq$ arg $z \leqq \beta$, *the series* $S(z)$ *is said to be an* **asymptotic expansion** *of* $f(z)$ *if, for each fixed n,*

$$\lim_{|z| \to \infty} z^n R_n(z) = 0.$$

We shall write $f(z) \sim S(z)$.

This definition applies to a power series in $1/z$ which converges for sufficiently large $|z|$, say for $|z| > R$. For then there is a constant M, depending on R only, such that for all values of arg z

$$|R_n(z)| < \frac{MR}{(|z| - R)|z|^n}.$$

THEOREM 26. *The product of two asymptotic expansions is an asymptotic expansion.*

PROOF. Suppose that, for a common range of arg z,

$$f(z) \sim S(z) = A_0 + \frac{A_1}{z} + \ldots + \frac{A_n}{z^n} + \ldots$$

and

$$g(z) \sim T(z) = B_0 + \frac{B_1}{z} + \ldots + \frac{B_n}{z^n} + \ldots$$

Then, for fixed n, as $|z| \to \infty$, †

$$f(z) - S_n(z) = o\,|z|^{-n}$$

and

$$g(z) - T_n(z) = o\,|z|^{-n}.$$

If now

$$C_m = A_0 B_m + A_1 B_{m-1} + \ldots + A_m B_0,$$

we have

$$f(z)g(z) = S_n(z)T_n(z) + o\,|z|^{-n}$$
$$= C_0 + \frac{C_1}{z} + \ldots + \frac{C_n}{z^n} + o\,|z|^{-n}$$

and this, being true for any fixed n, proves the theorem.

THEOREM 27. *The result of integrating an asymptotic expansion term-by-term is an asymptotic expansion.*

PROOF. We shall assume the variable to be real, as it usually is in practice.

Let $f(x) \sim S(x) = \dfrac{A_2}{x^2} + \dfrac{A_3}{x^3} + \ldots + \dfrac{A_n}{x^n} + \ldots,$

omitting the term which would give a logarithm.

For a fixed n, given ε, we can find x_0 such that

$$|f(x) - S_n(x)| < \varepsilon x^{-n} \text{ for } x \geqq x_0.$$

Then $\left| \displaystyle\int_x^\infty f(t)dt - \int_x^\infty S_n(t)dt \right| < \varepsilon \displaystyle\int_x^\infty \frac{dt}{t^n} = \frac{\varepsilon}{(n-1)x^{n-1}}.$

But $\displaystyle\int_x^\infty S_n(t)dt = \frac{A_2}{x} + \frac{A_3}{2x^2} + \ldots + \frac{A_n}{(n-1)x^{n-1}}$ and so

$$\int_x^\infty f(t)dt \sim \frac{A_2}{x} + \frac{A_3}{2x^2} + \ldots + \frac{A_n}{(n-1)x^{n-1}} + \ldots$$

which is what we set out to prove.

† For the o-notation, see Hyslop, *Infinite Series*, p. 14.

The question of uniqueness of asymptotic expansions is answered by two statements

THEOREM 28 (a) *For a given range of arg z, a function cannot have more than one asymptotic expansion.*

(b) *A series can be the asymptotic expansion of more than one function.*

PROOF. For (a), suppose that, for $\alpha \leqq \arg z \leqq \beta$,

$$f(z) \sim \sum_{n=0}^{\infty} A_n z^{-n} \text{ and } f(z) \sim \sum_{n=0}^{\infty} B_n z^{-n}.$$

Then, for fixed n, as $|z| \to \infty$,

$$(A_0 - B_0)z^n + (A_1 - B_1)z^{n-1} + \ldots + (A_n - B_n) \to 0,$$

and so $\qquad A_0 = B_0, \quad A_1 = B_1, \ldots$

For (b), a series can be the asymptotic expansion of both $f(z)$ and $g(z)$ so long as, for each fixed n,

$$z^n\{f(z) - g(z)\} \to 0 \quad \text{as} \quad |z| \to \infty.$$

This would be true, for example, if $f(z) - g(z) = e^{-z}$ for $\frac{1}{4}\pi \leqq \arg z \leqq \frac{1}{4}\pi$.

49. Asymptotic expansion of Bessel functions. A powerful method of approximating asymptotically to a known function is illustrated by the following expansion of $J_\nu(z)$.

THEOREM 29. $J_\nu(z)$ *is asymptotically*

$$\left(\frac{2}{\pi z}\right)^{\frac{1}{2}} \{\cos(z - \tfrac{1}{2}\nu\pi - \tfrac{1}{4}\pi)C_\nu(z) - \sin(z - \tfrac{1}{2}\nu\pi - \tfrac{1}{4}\pi)S_\nu(z)\}$$

where $\quad C_\nu(z) = 1 - \dfrac{(4\nu^2 - 1^2)(4\nu^2 - 3^2)}{2!(8z)^2} +$

$$+ \dfrac{(4\nu^2 - 1^2)(4\nu^2 - 3^2)(4\nu^2 - 5^2)(4\nu^2 - 7^2)}{4!(8z)^4} - \ldots$$

and $S_\nu(z) = \dfrac{4\nu^2 - 1^2}{8z} - \dfrac{(4\nu^2 - 1^2)(4\nu^2 - 3^2)(4\nu^2 - 5^2)}{3!(8z)^3} + \ldots,$

provided that $-\pi < \arg z < \pi.$

PROOF. To shorten the detail, we shall give the proof for $\nu = 0$; the principles are the same for a general ν. We shall take z to be real and positive, writing x for z.

From § 44 we have the formula

$$\pi J_0(x) = \int_{-1}^{1} e^{ixt}(1 - t^2)^{-\frac{1}{2}}dt.$$

Let A, B, C, D be the points 1, -1, $-1 + i\eta$, $1 + i\eta$ respectively in the ζ-plane. Indent the rectangle $ABCD$ at A and B by quadrants of circles of small radius.

Take

$$\int e^{ix\zeta}(1 - \zeta^2)^{-\frac{1}{2}}d\zeta$$

round the indented rectangle in the counter-clockwise sense, letting the radii of the indentations tend to 0 and the height η of the rectangle to infinity. The many-valued function $(1 - \zeta^2)^{-\frac{1}{2}}$ is defined to have its positive value for ζ on AB.

The integrand being regular inside the rectangle, the integral is zero by Cauchy's theorem.

As just stated, the integral along BA gives $\pi J_0(x)$. As $\eta \to \infty$, the integral along DC tends to zero, in virtue of the negative exponential. From now onwards $\int_{AD}$ and $\int_{BC}$ will denote integrals along these *infinite* vertical sides.

On AD put $\zeta = 1 + iu$.

Then $(1 - \zeta^2)^{-\frac{1}{2}} = (2 + iu)^{-\frac{1}{2}}(e^{-\frac{1}{2}\pi i}u)^{-\frac{1}{2}}$, and $d\zeta = idu$.

Thus, $\int_{AD} = e^{\frac{3}{4}\pi i}\int_0^{\infty} e^{ix-ux}u^{-\frac{1}{2}}(2 + iu)^{-\frac{1}{2}}du$.

Put $ux = v$, and we have

$$\int_{AD} = \frac{e^{i(x+\frac{3}{4}\pi)}}{\sqrt{(2x)}}\int_0^{\infty} e^{-v}v^{-\frac{1}{2}}\left(1 + \frac{iv}{2x}\right)^{-\frac{1}{2}} dv. \qquad (49.1)$$

The general term of the binomial expansion of $\left(1 + \dfrac{iv}{2x}\right)^{-\frac{1}{2}}$ is

$$(-1)^n \frac{1 \cdot 3 \ldots (2n-1)}{2^n n!} \left(\frac{iv}{2x}\right)^n$$

and the remainder after the term in v^n is less than
$$K(v/x)^{n+1},$$
where K depends only on n.

The contribution to the integral on the right-hand side of (49.1) of the term in v^n is

$$\left(-\frac{i}{4x}\right)^n \frac{1 \cdot 3 \ldots (2n-1)}{n!} \Gamma(n + \tfrac{1}{2})$$
$$= \left(-\frac{i}{8x}\right)^n \frac{1^2 \cdot 3^2 \ldots (2n-1)^2}{n!} \sqrt{\pi},$$

and the contribution of the remainder term is less than K/x^{n+1}, where again K depends only on n and is independent of x.

Hence the integral on the right-hand side of (49.1) takes the form
$$\sqrt{\pi}\{C_0(x) + iS_0(x)\}$$
and we have shown that the series $C_0(x)$ and $S_0(x)$ have the asymptotic property.

Similarly, on BC put $\zeta = -1 + iu$, and then $u = v/x$, giving

$$(1 - \zeta^2)^{-\frac{1}{2}} = (2 - iu)^{-\frac{1}{2}} e^{-\frac{1}{4}\pi i} u^{-\frac{1}{2}},$$
$$\int_{BC} = e^{\frac{1}{4}\pi i} \int_0^\infty e^{-ix - ux} u^{-\frac{1}{2}} (2 - iu)^{-\frac{1}{2}} du$$
$$= \frac{e^{-ix + \frac{1}{4}\pi i}}{\sqrt{(2x)}} \int_0^\infty e^{-v} v^{-\frac{1}{2}} \left(1 - \frac{iv}{2x}\right)^{-\frac{1}{2}} dv$$
$$\sim \frac{e^{-ix + \frac{1}{4}\pi i}}{\sqrt{(2x)}} \sqrt{\pi}\{C_0 - iS_0\},$$

by expanding the binomial as before.

Collecting the integrals along the sides of the rectangle and remembering that their sum is zero, we find

$$J_0(x) = -\frac{1}{\pi}\int_{AD} + \frac{1}{\pi}\int_{BC}$$

$$\sim \frac{1}{\sqrt{(2\pi x)}}\left[\{(\cos + i\sin)(x - \tfrac{1}{4}\pi)\}\{C_0(x) + iS_0(x)\}\right.$$
$$\left. + \{(\cos - i\sin)(x - \tfrac{1}{4}\pi)\}\{C_0(x) - iS_0(x)\}\right]$$

$$\sim \left(\frac{2}{\pi x}\right)^{\frac{1}{2}}\{\cos(x - \tfrac{1}{4}\pi)\,C_0(x) - \sin(x - \tfrac{1}{4}\pi)S_0(x)\},$$

and this is what we set out to prove.

The reader will now appreciate the following statement in general terms of a powerful method of finding an asymptotic expansion of a given function. If we have a contour integral representing the function, deform (if necessary) the contour into such a shape that on parts of it the integrand can be expanded in powers of $1/x$ together with a remainder term. We look to this decomposition to provide the series in powers of $1/x$ which forms the asymptotic expansion.

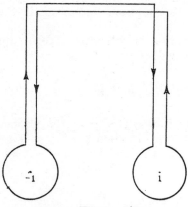

Fig. 3.

For the function $J_\nu(x)$, we could start from the integral of § 45 taken along a figure-of-eight contour round -1 and 1. The figure-of-eight can be deformed into the shape shown in Fig. 3, and the lengths of the vertical sides made to tend to infinity.

The integrand can be expanded in powers of $1/x$ along the vertical lines as in our discussion of $J_0(x)$.

The proof given for the asymptotic expansion of $J_0(x)$ rests essentially on manipulation of contour integrals. By using the expression of $J_0(x)$ as an integral along the real axis we were able to shorten the argument which the figure-of-eight would have entailed.

50. Asymptotic solutions of differential equations.

Equations having an irregular singularity at infinity are of common occurrence (for instance, linear equations with constant coefficients). The study of the behaviour of solutions of such equations for large values of x is therefore often necessary. The example of § 47 has already shown how an asymptotic expansion of a solution can be derived directly from the differential equation. As a further illustration we now obtain asymptotic expansions of solutions of Bessel's equation, finding again the series $C_\nu(x)$ and $S_\nu(x)$ of § 49.

Bessel's equation, written in a form appropriate for study of large values of x, is

$$y'' + \frac{1}{x} y' + \left(1 - \frac{\nu^2}{x^2}\right) y = 0.$$

Make the substitution $y = e^{ix}u$, the e^{ix} being suggested as a solution of the equation $y'' + y = 0$ got by ignoring the terms in $1/x$ and $1/x^2$.

The equation for u is found to be

$$u'' + \left(2i + \frac{1}{x}\right) u' + \left(\frac{i}{x} - \frac{\nu^2}{x^2}\right) u = 0.$$

Substitute $u = x^\sigma v$ and choose σ so that the coefficient of v has no term in $1/x$. We find that $\sigma = -\frac{1}{2}$, and that the equation for v is

$$v'' + 2iv' + \frac{\frac{1}{4} - \nu^2}{x^2}\, v = 0.$$

Try to solve this formally by writing

$$v = a_0 + \frac{a_1}{x} + \ldots + \frac{a_n}{x^n} + \ldots,$$

and we find the recurrence relation

$$2i(n + 1)a_{n+1} = \{n(n + 1) + \tfrac{1}{4} - \nu^2\}a_n.$$

This gives for v a constant multiple of the series

$$1 + \frac{1^2 - 4\nu^2}{8ix} + \frac{(1^2 - 4\nu^2)(3^2 - 4\nu^2)}{2!(8ix)^2} + \frac{(1^2 - 4\nu^2)(3^2 - 4\nu^2)(5^2 - 4\nu^2)}{3!(8ix)^3} + \ldots$$

which is precisely the $C_\nu(x) + iS_\nu(x)$ of theorem 29. Changing the sign of i we have another solution, and hence as two solutions of Bessel's equation any constant multiples of

$$x^{-\frac{1}{2}}\{C_\nu(x) \cos x - S_\nu(x) \sin x\}$$
or of
$$x^{-\frac{1}{2}}\{C_\nu(x) \sin x + S_\nu(x) \cos x\}.$$

To find what combination of these two solutions will yield a prescribed solution such as the function $J_\nu(x)$ we should need to know independently the first term in the asymptotic expansion of $J_\nu(x)$.

51. Calculation of zeros of $J_0(x)$.

As an illustration of the use of asymptotic expansions we shall show how to approximate to the large zeros of Bessel functions with any required degree of accuracy. As before we shall take $J_0(x)$, for which the detail is simpler.

From the asymptotic expansion found in theorem 29, $J_0(x)$ is zero when

$$\cot\left(x - \frac{1}{4}\pi\right) = \frac{S_0(x)}{C_0(x)} = \frac{-\dfrac{1}{8x} + \dfrac{75}{1024x^3} - \cdots}{1 - \dfrac{9}{128x^2} + \cdots}.$$

If x is large and positive, this has a root a little greater than $(n - \frac{1}{4})\pi$, say $(n - \frac{1}{4})\pi + \alpha$. Then

$$\tan\alpha = \frac{1}{8x} - \frac{33}{512x^3} + \cdots,$$

and so

$$\alpha = \tan\alpha - \tfrac{1}{3}\tan^3\alpha + \cdots$$

$$= \frac{1}{8x} - \frac{25}{384x^3} + \cdots$$

This gives by successive approximation that, if n is a large integer, $J_0(x)$ vanishes for

$$x = \left(n - \tfrac{1}{4}\right)\pi + \frac{1}{8(n - \frac{1}{4})\pi} - \frac{31}{384(n - \frac{1}{4})^3\pi^3} + \cdots,$$

and, by retaining higher powers in the asymptotic expansion for $J_0(x)$ originally quoted, we can approximate as closely as we like to the zeros.

THE LAPLACE TRANSFORM.

We shall outline a useful technique for solving a linear differential equation having constant coefficients. It will be convenient to take the independent variable to be t (not x), where $t \geqq 0$. Suppose that we seek the solution $y(t)$ of the differential equation

$$a_0 y^{(n)} + a_1 y^{(n-1)} + \ldots + a_{n-1} y' + a_n y = r(t) \qquad (1)$$

such that, for $t = 0$,

$$y = y_0, \ y' = y_1, \ \ldots, y^{(n-1)} = y_{n-1}.$$

The existence and uniqueness of $y(t)$ is assured by § 6.

DEFINITION. Let

$$\varphi(p) = \int_0^\infty e^{-pt} f(t) dt,$$

it being assumed that a number p_0 exists such that the integral converges for $p > p_0$. Then $\varphi(p)$ is called the *Laplace transform* of $f(t)$ and is usually written

$$\mathscr{L}\{f(t)\} \text{ or } \mathscr{L}(f).$$

The Laplace transform has the following properties.

(1) $\mathscr{L}(f_1 + \ldots + f_n) = \mathscr{L}(f_1) + \ldots + \mathscr{L}(f_n).$

(2) $\mathscr{L}(cf) = c\mathscr{L}(f)$, if c is constant.

These two properties show that $\mathscr{L}$ is a *linear operator*.

(3) $\mathscr{L}\{e^{-at} f(t)\} = \varphi(p + a).$

(4) If $\mathscr{L}\{f_1(t)\} = \varphi_1(p)$ and $\mathscr{L}\{f_2(t)\} = \varphi_2(p)$, then

$$\varphi_1(p)\varphi_2(p) = \mathscr{L}\left\{ \int_0^t f_1(u) f_2(t - u) du \right\}.$$

(5) A continuous function is uniquely determined by its Laplace transform.

The proofs of (1), (2), (3) are easy. To prove (4), we have, by inverting the order of integration in the repeated integral,

$$\mathscr{L}\left\{\int_0^t f_1(u)f_2(t-u)du\right\}$$
$$= \int_0^\infty e^{-pt}dt \int_0^t f_1(u)f_2(t-u)du$$
$$= \int_0^\infty f_1(u)du \int_u^\infty e^{-pt}f_2(t-u)dt$$
$$= \int_0^\infty f_1(u)du \int_0^\infty e^{-p(u+v)}f_2(v)dv$$
$$= \varphi_1(p)\varphi_2(p).$$

The property (5), which is essential in justifying the use of Laplace transforms, needs a more substantial investigation. This will be given after we have explained the manipulative detail.

The following table is a short list of transforms of common functions.

$f(t)$	$\varphi(p)$
1	$\dfrac{1}{p}$
e^{at}	$\dfrac{1}{p-a}$
$\dfrac{t^{n-1}}{(n-1)!}$	$\dfrac{1}{p^n}$
$\dfrac{t^{n-1}e^{at}}{(n-1)!}$	$\dfrac{1}{(p-a)^n}$
$\sin at$	$\dfrac{a}{p^2+a^2}$
$\cos at$	$\dfrac{p}{p^2+a^2}$
$\dfrac{t\sin at}{2a}$	$\dfrac{p}{(p^2+a^2)^2}$
$\dfrac{1}{2a^3}(\sin at - at\cos at)$	$\dfrac{1}{(p^2+a^2)^2}$

The method of solution by transforms. Multiply the differential equation (1) by e^{-pt} and integrate from 0 to ∞ (assuming that p can be chosen so as to make the integrals converge). Integrating by parts and using the initial values of $y(t)$ and its derivatives, we have

$$\int_0^\infty e^{-pt} y' dt = -y_0 + p \int_0^\infty e^{-pt} y\, dt,$$

$$\int_0^\infty e^{-pt} y'' dt = -y_1 - py_0 + p^2 \int_0^\infty e^{-pt} y\, dt,$$

and, generally, for $s \leqq n$,

$$\int_0^\infty e^{-pt} y^{(s)} dt = -y_{s-1} - py_{s-2} - \ldots - p^{s-1} y_0 + p^s \int_0^\infty e^{-pt} y\, dt.$$

So y will satisfy the equation (1) with the given initial conditions if

$$(a_0 p^n + a_1 p^{n-1} + \ldots + a_n)\mathscr{L}\{y(t)\}$$
$$= y_0(a_0 p^{n-1} + a_1 p^{n-2} + \ldots + a_{n-1})$$
$$+ y_1(a_0 p^{n-2} + a_1 p^{n-3} + \ldots + a_{n-2}) + \ldots$$
$$+ y_{n-2}(a_0 p + a_1) + y_{n-1} a_0 + \mathscr{L}\{r(t)\} \tag{2}$$

The equation (2) is called the *subsidiary equation*. A table of transforms is used to find $\mathscr{L}\{r(t)\}$ from $r(t)$, and then to find $y(t)$ from $\mathscr{L}\{y(t)\}$.

Illustration.

Solve the equation

$$y''' - 3y' + 2y = 3e^t,$$

given that $y(0) = 0$, $y'(0) = 1$, $y''(0) = 2$.

The Laplace transform of the equation is

$$(p^3 - 3p + 2)\mathscr{L}(y) = p + 2 + \frac{3}{p-1},$$

giving

$$\mathscr{L}(y) = \frac{1}{(p-1)^2} + \frac{3}{(p-1)^3(p+2)}$$

$$= -\frac{1}{9(p+2)} + \frac{1}{9(p-1)} + \frac{2}{3(p-1)^2} + \frac{1}{(p-1)^3}.$$

From the table of transforms, the solution is

$$y = -\tfrac{1}{9}e^{-2t} + \tfrac{1}{9}e^t + \tfrac{2}{3}te^t + \tfrac{1}{2}t^2e^t.$$

In the last step we assume the fact, still to be proved, that y is uniquely determined by $\mathscr{L}(y)$.

The uniqueness theorem. To prove the property (5) above, we need a lemma (Lerch's theorem).

LEMMA. *If $\psi(x)$ is continuous for $0 \leqq x \leqq 1$, and*

$$\int_0^1 x^n\psi(x)dx = 0 \quad for \quad n = 0, 1, 2, \ldots,$$
then $\psi(x) \equiv 0$ *for* $0 \leqq x \leqq 1$.

PROOF. If the conclusion is false, there is an interval (a, b) with $0 < a < b < 1$ such that $\psi(x) \geqq k > 0$ (or $\psi(x) \leqq -k < 0$) for $a \leqq x \leqq b$.

We proceed to define a polynomial $p(x)$ for which

$$\int_0^1 p(x)\,\psi(x)dx > 0$$

and this will contradict the hypothesis.

Let c be the larger of ab, $(1 - a)(1 - b)$, and let

$$q(x) = 1 + \frac{1}{c}(b - x)(x - a)$$

Then $q(x) > 1$ for $a < x < b$, and $0 < q(x) < 1$ for $0 < x < a$ and $b < x < 1$.

If we choose a sufficiently large integer m, the polynomial $p(x) = \{q(x)\}^m$ will take arbitrarily large values in $a < x < b$ and arbitrarily small values in $0 < x < a$ and $b < x < 1$.

So we can make

$$\int_0^1 p(x)\psi(x)dx > 0$$

and the lemma is proved.

THEOREM. *Not more than one continuous function $f(t)$ can satisfy the equation*

$$\varphi(p) = \int_0^\infty e^{-pt}f(t)dt$$

for all $p \geqq k$.

PROOF. It is sufficient to show that, if $\varphi(p) = 0$ for all $p \geq k$, then $f(t) \equiv 0$.

Let $p = k + n$. Integrating by parts, we have

$$n \int_0^\infty e^{-nt}\,dt \int_0^t e^{-ku}f(u)du = \int_0^\infty e^{-(k+n)t}f(t)dt$$

and so

$$\int_0^\infty e^{-nt}g(t)dt = 0 \quad \text{for } n = 0, 1, 2, \ldots,$$

where

$$g(t) = \int_0^t e^{-ku}f(u)du.$$

In the lemma, write $x = e^{-t}$, $\psi(x) = g\{\log(1/x)\}$. Then $\psi(x)$ is continuous for $0 < x \leq 1$ and $\psi(0)$ can be defined as the limit of $\psi(x)$ as x tends to 0 through positive values.

We have

$$\int_0^1 x^n\psi(x)dx = 0 \quad \text{for } n = 0, 1, 2, \ldots.$$

By the lemma, $\psi(x) \equiv 0$, that is to say

$$g(t) = \int_0^t e^{-ku}f(u)du \equiv 0 \quad \text{for } t \geq 0.$$

So $0 = g'(t) = e^{-kt}f(t)$ for all $t \geq 0$ and hence $f(t) = 0$ for all $t \geq 0$.

The method of transforms can be applied to much more general problems, for instance to solve important types of partial differential equations.

Examples.

Solve the following equations, where $y_0, y_1, \ldots$ are the values for $t = 0$ of $y, y', \ldots$

1. $y''' - 2y'' + y' = 2.$ $y_0 = 2, y_1 = 1, y_2 = -1.$
2. $y'' - y' - 2y = 60e^t \sin 2t.$ $y_0 = y_1 = 0.$
3. $y'''' - y = 0.$ $y_0 = 1, y_1 = y_2 = y_3 = 0.$
4. $y'''' - 2y'' + y = 12te^t.$ $y_0 = y_2 = \frac{1}{2}, y_1 = 0, y_3 = -3.$

5. $x'' + (a + b)y' - abx = 0,$ $x_0 = y_0 = 0,$
   $y'' - (a + b)x' - aby = 0.$ $x_1 = 1, \ y_1 = 0.$

6. $x'' = ay',$ $x_0 = y_0 = x_1 = y_1 = 0.$
   $y'' = b - ax'.$

LINES OF FORCE AND EQUIPOTENTIAL SURFACES.

The mathematical analysis which follows has been given a physical title because it is to many people the most suggestive; they intuitively picture the differential equations as representing a situation such as an electrostatic field.

The equation of § 2 can be written in the notation of differentials as

$$P dx + Q dy = 0,$$

where P and Q are functions of x and y. If P and Q satisfy appropriate conditions the equation will possess a solution of the form

$$u(x, y) = A.$$

If u is differentiable,

$$u_x dx + u_y dy = 0,$$

and, comparing this with the original equation, we have

$$u_x = \mu P, \ u_y = \mu Q,$$

where μ is a function of x and y which we can call an integrating factor of the original equation.

We now inquire into the possible extension from two variables to three. When does the equation

$$P dx + Q dy + R dz = 0$$

(where P, Q, R are functions of x, y, z) possess a solution

$$u(x, y, z) = A?$$

We keep in mind the geometrical meaning. The differential equation states that the line-element (dx, dy, dz) is perpendicular to the direction (P, Q, R), and the equation $u(x, y, z) = A$ represents a family of surfaces.

THEOREM. *Suppose that P, Q, R are differentiable functions of x, y, z in a domain of values of x, y, z. A necessary and sufficient condition that the differential equation*

$$Pdx + Qdy + Rdz = 0 \qquad (1)$$

has a solution

$$u(x, y, z) = A$$

is that

$$P(Q_z - R_y) + Q(R_x - P_z) + R(P_y - Q_x) \equiv 0 \qquad (2)$$

PROOF. *Necessity.* We have, for some integrating factor $\mu(x, y, z)$,

$$u_x = \mu P, \quad u_y = \mu Q, \quad u_z = \mu R.$$

So

$$\mu_z Q + \mu Q_z = u_{yz} = u_{zy} = \mu_y R + \mu R_y$$

and two similar results for u_{zx}, u_{xy}.

Multiplying the equations by P, Q, R and adding, we have the condition (2).

Sufficiency. The proof is rather longer but it embodies a process of actually finding the solution.

Keep one of x, y, z constant. Say it is z and integrate

$$Pdx + Qdy = 0,$$

giving

$$u = A,$$

where u is a function of x, y, z such that, for some μ,

$$u_x = \mu P, \quad u_y = \mu Q.$$

Now let z vary and put

$$u = f(z).$$

This gives

$$u_x dx + u_y dy + \{u_z - f'(z)\}dz = 0.$$

This is the same equation as (1) if

$$u_z - f'(z) = \mu R.$$

The function f can be determined if $u_z - \mu R$ is a function of z and f (that is, u) alone.

A sufficient condition for this is that the Jacobian of u and $u_z - \mu R$ with respect to x and y is zero. This gives

$$u_x \frac{\partial}{\partial y}(u_z - \mu R) - u_y \frac{\partial}{\partial x}(u_z - \mu R) \equiv 0.$$

Now it is easy to verify that, if the equation (1) is multiplied through by μ, the relation (2) holds for the new coefficients,

$$\mu P\{(\mu Q)_z - (\mu R)_y\}$$
$$+ \mu Q\{(\mu R)_x - (\mu P)_z\} + \mu R\{(\mu P)_y - (\mu Q)_x\} \equiv 0.$$

Since $\mu P = u_x$ and $\mu Q = u_y$, this identity is the same as the preceding one.

Illustration.

Solve the equation

$$(y + z)z\, dx - zx\, dy + xy\, dz = 0.$$

The condition of integrability (2) is satisfied. Keeping x constant, we obtain $y = Az$. Put then $y = zf(x)$, and differentiate,

$$zf'(x)dx - dy + f(x)dz = 0.$$

Comparing with the original equation, we find

$$xf'(x) = f(x) + 1$$

Hence $f(x) + 1 = Ax$, and the solution is

$$y + z = Azx.$$

The interpretation of the equation (1), if the condition of integrability (2) is not satisfied, is beyond the scope of this book.

Examples.

Solve the equations

1. $(y - z)dx + (z - x)dy + (x - y)dz = 0.$
2. $(y^2 + z^2)dx + (z^2 + x^2)dy - 2z(x + y)dz = 0.$
3. $(1 + yz)dx + x(z - x)dy - (1 + xy)dz = 0.$
4. $(y^2 + yz + z^2)dx + (z^2 + zx + x^2)dy + (x^2 + xy + y^2)\, dz = 0.$

Simultaneous equations. Consider now the equations

$$\frac{dx}{P} = \frac{dy}{Q} = \frac{dz}{R},$$

where P, Q, R are functions of x, y, z. They are the same as the simultaneous equations on page 9, written in symmetrical form. The solution may be expected to consist of a curve through a given point (x_0, y_0, z_0), the curves for different initial points (x_0, y_0, z_0) forming a doubly-infinite family.

In the case of integrability of the equation

$$Pdx + Qdy + Rdz = 0,$$

the surfaces forming its solution cut orthogonally the curves of the doubly-infinite family. (The reader will recognize lines of force and equipotential surfaces.)

Methods of solution. The most common device when P, Q, R are simple functions is to write

$$\frac{dx}{P} = \frac{dy}{Q} = \frac{dz}{R} = \frac{\lambda dx + \mu dy + \nu dz}{\lambda P + \mu Q + \nu R},$$

and choose the multipliers λ, μ, ν so that either the denominator is 0 or the numerator is the derivative of the denominator.

Illustrations.

(1) $$\frac{dx}{bz - cy} = \frac{dy}{cx - az} = \frac{dz}{ay - bx},$$

where a, b, c are constants.

Each ratio $= \dfrac{a\,dx + b\,dy + c\,dz}{0}$

and also $= \dfrac{x\,dx + y\,dy + z\,dz}{0}.$

These give

$$ax + by + cz = A$$

and

$$x^2 + y^2 + z^2 = B,$$

a doubly-infinite family of curves (in fact, all circles with centres on the line

$$\frac{x}{a} = \frac{y}{b} = \frac{z}{c}$$

lying in planes perpendicular to this line).

(2) $$\frac{dx}{y+z} = \frac{dy}{z+x} = \frac{dz}{x+y}.$$

Each ratio $= \dfrac{d(x+y+z)}{2(x+y+z)}$

and each $= -\dfrac{dx-dy}{x-y} = -\dfrac{dz-dx}{z-x}.$

We obtain the curves as intersections of the surfaces

$$(x+y+z)(x-y)^2 = A$$

by the planes

$$(x-y)/(z-x) = B.$$

(3) $$\frac{dx}{1} = \frac{dy}{c} = \frac{dz}{x \sin (y - cx)},$$

where c is constant.

An obvious integral is $y - cx = A$. This gives

$$dx = \frac{dz}{x \sin A}$$

and so

$$z = \tfrac{1}{2}x^2 \sin A + B.$$

If we now put back $A = y - cx$, we find by differentiating that

$$z = \tfrac{1}{2}x^2 \sin (y - cx) + B$$

is in fact a second solution.

Examples.

Solve $dx/P = dy/Q = dz/R$, with the values of P, Q, R given in each of 5—7.

5. $x(y - z)$, $y(z - x)$, $z(x - y)$.

6. x, y, $\sqrt{(x^2 + y^2)}$.

7. $z(x + 2y)$, $- z(y + 2x)$, $y^2 - x^2$.

8. For each of the following families of curves examine whether there is a family of orthogonal surfaces:

(i) straight lines intersecting the lines

$$y = 0, \ z = c \ \text{and} \ x = 0, \ z = -c;$$

(ii) cubic curves $y = ax^2$, $y^2 = bzx$, where a and b vary.

SOLUTIONS OF EXAMPLES

CHAPTER I.

1. $3 + \eta = Ae^{6\xi}(3 - \eta)$ with ξ, η as specified.

2. $(A + 2 \tan^{1/2} x)/(A \tan x + \tan^{3/2} x)$.

7. $\frac{1}{2}x^2 \ (x \leq 2)$, $2e^{x-2} \ (x > 2)$.

8. (i) $\frac{1}{3}x^3 + \frac{1}{12}x^4 + \frac{1}{60}x^5$.

   (ii) $y = \frac{1}{2}x^2 + \frac{1}{8}x^4 + \frac{1}{30}x^5$, $z = 1 + \frac{1}{2}x^2 + \frac{1}{6}x^3 + \frac{1}{40}x^5$.

9. Ince, Text, p. 36.

10. If $|y| \leq x^2$, $f(x, y) = 2y/x \ (x \neq 0)$, $= 0 (x = 0)$.
    If $y > x^2$, $f(x, y) = 2x$; if $y < -x^2$, $f(x, y) = -2x$.

CHAPTER II.

1. $A_1e^x + A_2e^{-x} + B_1 \cos x + B_2 \sin x - \frac{1}{4}x \sin x$.

2. $Ae^{-2x} + Be^x + Cxe^x + \frac{1}{2}x^2e^x$.

3. $A \cos \left\{ \dfrac{b}{a} \log (ax + 1) \right\} + B \sin \left\{ \dfrac{b}{a} \log (ax + 1) \right\}$.

4. $Ax + Be^x + x^2 + x + 1$.

5. $A(1 + 2x^2) + Bx\sqrt{(1 + x^2)}$.

6. $Ae^x + Bx^2$.

7. $x(Ae^x + B) - x^2$.

8. $x(-\frac{1}{3}x^3 - x + A) + (x^2 + 1)(\frac{1}{2}x^2 + B)$.

9. $xe^t = x_0 + \frac{5}{2}t - y_0t - t^2 + \frac{1}{2}z_0t^2 + \frac{1}{4}t^3$,
   $ye^t = y_0 + 2t - z_0t - \frac{3}{4}t^2$,
   $ze^t = z_0 + \frac{3}{2}t$.

11. $A \cos x^2 + B \sin x^2$.

12. $A \cos x + B \tan x + \frac{1}{2} \sec x$.

13. $\{A \log (1 - \sin x) + \frac{1}{2}A \sin x + B\}/(1 + \sin x)$.

14. $\{x + \sin (t - x) - t \cos (t - x)\}/t^2$.

15. $(n + 2)(1 + x)y = x^{n+2} + (n + 2)(Ax^{n+1} + B)$.

16. $x^3y = \pi(x \cos x - \sin x) - \pi^2(x \sin x + \cos x)$.

17. (Sufficiency). There are constants $c_1, \ldots, c_n$, not all 0, such that

$$c_1 a_{i1} + \ldots + c_n a_{in} = 0 \quad (1 \leqq i \leqq n).$$

Multiply the ith equation by c_i and add. We have

$$\int_a^b (c_1 u_1 + \ldots + c_n u_n)^2 dx = 0.$$

18. $(Au_1 + Bu_2)/(u_1 u_2' - u_1' u_2)$.   **19.** $Axe^x + Be^{-x}/x$.

20. $2p_1 p_2 + p_2' = 0$.

CHAPTER IV.

Independent solutions of each of $1-12$ are given in finite form when a series is so expressible.

1. $z^{\frac{1}{2}}$, $(1 - z)^{\frac{1}{2}}$.

2. $1 + 12z^2 + \dfrac{48}{5} z^4 - \dfrac{64}{15} z^6 + \cdots$,

$$z^{\frac{3}{2}} \left\{ 1 + \frac{3}{2} z^2 - \frac{1 \cdot 3}{2 \cdot 4} z^4 + \frac{1 \cdot 3 \cdot 5}{2 \cdot 4 \cdot 6} z^6 - \cdots \right\}.$$

3. Cf 22   **4.** $1 + z$, $z^2(1 - z)^{-1}$.

5. z, $z^2 + z \log z$.

6. $w_1 = \sum_0^\infty \dfrac{z^{2n}}{(n!)^2}$,

$$w_2 = w_1 \log z - \left\{ z^2 + \frac{z^4}{(2!)^2}\left(1 + \frac{1}{2}\right) + \frac{z^6}{(3!)^2}\left(1 + \frac{1}{2} + \frac{1}{3}\right) + \cdots \right\}.$$

7. $1 + \dfrac{z^4}{2 \cdot 3 \cdot 4} + \dfrac{z^8}{2 \cdot 3 \cdot 4 \cdot 6 \cdot 7 \cdot 8} + \cdots$,

$$z + \frac{z^5}{3 \cdot 4 \cdot 5} + \cdots, \quad z^2 + \frac{z^6}{4 \cdot 5 \cdot 6} + \cdots$$

8. $w_1 = \sum_1^\infty \dfrac{z^n}{1 \cdot 2^2 \ldots (n - 1)^2 n}$,

$$w_2 = w_1 \log z + 1 - \sum_1^\infty \frac{z^n}{1 \cdot 2^2 \ldots (n-1)^2 n} \left(\frac{2}{1} + \frac{2}{2} + \ldots + \frac{2}{n-1} + \frac{1}{n}\right).$$

9. $z(1 - z)^{-1}$, $z^{-1}(1 - z)$.

10. $z^{\frac{1}{2}}$, $z^{\frac{1}{2}}(1 - \frac{1}{2}z)^{\frac{1}{2}}$.

11. e^{-z^2}, $e^{-z^2} \log z$.

12. $6z + 4kz^2 + k^2z^3$, $z^5 \left(1 + \dfrac{2}{5 \cdot 1} kz + \dfrac{2 \cdot 3}{5 \cdot 6 \cdot 1 \cdot 2} k^2z^2 + \ldots\right)$.

13. $w_1 = \sum\limits_0^\infty \dfrac{z^n}{n!\,k(k+1)\ldots(k+n-1)}$,

$\quad w_2 = z^{1-k} \sum\limits_0^\infty \dfrac{z^n}{n!\,(2-k)(3-k)\ldots(n+1-k)}$.

For $k = 1$, $w_2 = w_1 \log z - \sum\limits_1^\infty \dfrac{2z^n}{(n!)^2} \left(1 + \dfrac{1}{2} + \ldots + \dfrac{1}{n}\right)$.

For $k = \frac{1}{2}$, $w_1 = \cosh 2\sqrt{z}$, $w_2 = \frac{1}{2}\sinh 2\sqrt{z}$.

14. $u = x(1-x)^{-2}$, $(1-x)^{-1} + u \log x$.

16. $A \sum\limits_0^\infty \dfrac{(-2x^2)^n}{(2n-3)(2n-1)(2n+1)} + B \dfrac{(1+2x^2)^2}{x}$. $0 < |x| < \dfrac{1}{\sqrt{2}}$.

17. $w_1 = \sum\limits_0^\infty (-1)^n \dfrac{p(p+1)\ldots(p+n-1)}{n!\,(p+q)\ldots(p+q+n-1)} z^n$,

$\qquad w_2 = z^{1-p-q} \sum\limits_0^\infty \dfrac{(1-q)\ldots(n-q)}{n!\,(p+q-2)\ldots(p+q-n-1)} z^n$.

If $p + q = 1$, second solution is

$w_1 \log z + \sum\limits_1^\infty \left\{(-1)^n \dfrac{p(p+1)\ldots(p+n-1)}{(n!)^2} \times \right.$

$\left. \left(\dfrac{1}{p} + \dfrac{1}{p+1} + \ldots + \dfrac{1}{p+n-1} - \dfrac{2}{1} - \dfrac{2}{2} \ldots - \dfrac{2}{n}\right) z^n\right\}$.

18. Recurrence relation is $(n-1)nc_n + a(n-1)c_{n-1} + bc_{n-2} = 0$.
Put $c_n = d_n/n!$
Solution of equation is e^{pz}/z, where p is a root of $p^2 + ap + b = 0$.

19. $(1+z)(A \cos \log z + B \sin \log z)$.

20. $3(4n+3)a_n = \sum\limits_{r+s=n-1} a_r a_s$. By induction $a_n \leqq 12^{-n}$.
For last part cf Ch I, ex. 11.

CHAPTER V.

7. Put $t = 1 - u$ in (28.1).

CHAPTER VIII.

1. $z^{\frac{1}{2}}\{AJ_{k+\frac{1}{2}}(cz) + BJ_{-k-\frac{1}{2}}(cz)\}.$

2. $z^{\frac{1}{2}}\{AJ_{\frac{1}{3}}(\frac{2}{3}z^{\frac{3}{2}}) + BJ_{-\frac{1}{3}}(\frac{2}{3}z^{\frac{3}{2}})\}.$

5. Expand $J_\nu(bt)$ in series and integrate term-by-term. Transform the result by use of Chapter V, example 7.
$1/\sqrt{(a^2 + b^2)}.$

6. For the limiting process, see e.g. Bromwich, *Theory of Infinite Series*, p. 483.

APPENDIX I

1. $y = 3 + 2t - e^t.$

2. $y = 8e^{2t} - 5e^{-t} - e^t(3\cos 2t + 9\sin 2t).$

3. $y = \frac{1}{2}\cosh t + \frac{1}{2}\cos t.$

4. $y = e^{-t} + \frac{1}{2}e^t(t-1)^3.$

5. $x = \dfrac{\sin at - \sin bt}{a - b}, \quad y = \dfrac{\cos bt - \cos at}{a - b}\,(b \neq a).$

   If $a = b$, $x = t\cos at$, $y = t\sin at.$

6. $x = (b/a^2)(at - \sin at),\ y = (b/a^2)(1 - \cos at).$

APPENDIX II

1. $y - z = A(z - x).$

2. $x + y = A(xy - z^2).$

3. $z - x = A(1 + xy).$

4. $x + y + z = A(yz + zx + xy).$

5. $x + y + z = A, \quad xyz = B.$

6. $y = Ax, \quad x^2 + y^2 = (z + B)^2.$

7. $x^2 + y^2 + z^2 = A, \quad xy - z^2 = B.$

8. (i) No, (ii) Yes.

BIBLIOGRAPHY

Reference has already been made in the preface to the books in the series of University Mathematical Texts which are most closely related to this one.

Among the more comprehensive works which the reader may consult with profit are

L. BIEBERBACH, Theorie der Differentialgleichungen, 1930.

E. T. COPSON, An introduction to the theory of functions of a complex variable, 1935.

R. COURANT and D. HILBERT, Methods of mathematical physics (translated) 1953.

E. L. INCE, Ordinary differential equations, 1927.

H. and B. S. JEFFREYS, Methods of mathematical physics, 3rd ed., 1956.

C. J. DE LA VALLÉE POUSSIN, Cours d'analyse infinitesimale, vol. II, 1928.

G. VALIRON, Cours d'analyse II — Equations fonctionnelles, 1945.

INDEX

References are to pages